FIBROMYALGIA

HOPE
from a completely
NEW PERSPECTIVE

D1435213

William Glasser, M.D.

Cover Design

By

Terrence McWilliams

Disclaimer

This document is an original work of the author. It may include reference to information commonly known or freely available to the general public. Any resemblance to other published information is purely coincidental. The author has in no way attempted to use material not of his own origination.

ISBN: 0-9678444-2-8

Dedication

To Sue Brown for her many years of hard work for the William Glasser Institute and for her courage to share her life with the readers of this book.

Contents

Acknowledgements

First of all, I want to express appreciation for the work of my wife Carleen who shares everything I do and who has meticulously edited this book as she has all my last six books. I also want to thank all the people in the Institute office: Linda, who runs the operation, Pam, Helen, Zona, Bud, Gene and Sue. These people do far more than work in the office, they are dedicated to the ideas. Finally, my gratitude goes out to the hundreds of people who teach Choice Theory and Reality Therapy around the world. We are a connected group. It is a pleasure for me to be a part of it.

Foreword

Janice is an exceptionally attractive thirty-one-year-old woman who is brought into the emergency department late one evening by ambulance after swallowing a half of a bottle of mild antidepressants. She was attempting to "kill" herself after a fight with her boyfriend. When I finally manage to corner her obviously distraught parents to gain some insight into their daughter's problems, her mother blurts out: "I don't know what happened … this all started when she graduated from law school."

Melissa is a twenty-five-year-old hairdresser who waits over three hours to be seen in the emergency department on an unusually busy afternoon. Her medical diagnosis amounts to no more than a common cold. When I ask her if there is anything else I can do for her, she bursts into tears saying, "Yeah, you can kill my husband."

David is a sixty-eight-year-old retired cab driver who collects disability for a chronic back condition that has never truly been found to have a pathologic origin. When I greet him on his bed, he is so intoxicated that he cannot finish a sentence; and when I inquire into what brings him to the emergency department for the third night in a row, he slurs, "I don't know, Doc. I guess I just don't like being alone."

Each of these very sad stories is repeated literally thousands of times a day in all of our nation's emergency departments and physician's offices. They happen in every single community, rich and poor, Black and White, rural and urban. And while at first glance it might appear that these three people have nothing in common, on closer inspection I believe it becomes quite clear that they do.

These vignettes have three very similar threads: First, they are the stories of people who are in real pain, yet we in the medical community have an extraordinarily difficult time identifying anything but a small component of it—the physical part. Secondly, they are people who are not in pain because of something that "happened" to them but, rather, because of the choices they made. And finally—and most importantly—they are people who are in pain because they cannot connect in a meaningful way to some significant relationship in their lives. If they could do that effectively, they would not be sitting in my emergency room or my colleagues' offices.

Although the study of "pain" is actually quite new to the medical profession, it is receiving more attention every day. Indeed, it has even recently been mandated by some state legislatures as "the fifth vital sign." Yet, I am not here to debate differences between physical and psycho-logical pain. And I am not so sure that it really matters. What I do know is that no matter what kind of pain it is, we are notoriously poor in treating it.

We are even less successful if we cannot easily identify a cause, especially if it seems to be a lingering or chronic pain. It is one thing if little Johnny "fell from the tree" and has an arm shaped like a boomerang; it is quite another if Doris "aches all over," and every known test aimed at telling us why is negative. As physicians we are supposed to be able to identify pain, yet we are never really taught how. Is it how loud you yell? Is it how long you grimace? Is there a color scale to which you can point?

I don't think the argument over physical versus psychological pain gets us anywhere. Call it what you will, but don't waste too much time trying to figure out if it really exists because, in some form or other, it exists in the mind of the sufferer. In fact, I have been a practicing emergency physician in just about every setting imaginable over the past decade and I can only say this about pain: First, it is the single greatest reason that people go to see their health care provider. And second, to the sufferer, pain is similar to that old saying about pornography: "You may not know it when you see it but you always know it when you feel it." In my job, I don't really have to go looking for pain; it doesn't knock, it keeps barging in my door and there is no way to keep it out.

Almost twenty years ago, one of my delightfully subtle sisters marched into my room during what was probably becoming a rather annoying period of self-pity. She whacked me on the head with a dog-eared paperback and said, "Read this!" Living in a family of six rather mild-mannered females, I am not sure at that point in time if I really had much choice. Nevertheless, I did read it, and it turned out to be one of the most important things I have ever done. The book, as it turns out, was Dr. Glasser's landmark *Reality Therapy* and his message, I am happy to say, hit me far harder than her thump could have ever hoped to do.

A short while later I met Dr. Glasser, and so began a long personal journey where I have closely followed the evolution of his work and tried to implement it into my personal and professional life. While my career has evolved from an educator to a physician and now towards one of a health policy planner, I have tried to never wander too far from his mantra: *It's all about the choices we make.*

I firmly agree with Dr. Glasser that a major reason our health care system is in crisis today is because it is not organized to handle all the people in our society who are in pain. More importantly, it is a system which has very little understanding of the fact that a large number of people who interface with it every day are there for a single reason: the painful consequences of their inability to connect with an important relationship in their lives.

The Janices, Melissas and Davids I described above are really no different from the thousands upon thousands of Americans who pour into emergency departments and primary care settings every day. Some studies show that as many as forty to fifty percent of emergency visits are for non-urgent problems; others show that "behavioral problems" make up almost twenty-five percent of an ER's visits. Ask any general internist or family practitioner what proportion of their daily patient visits are encompassed by people truly needing their medical expertise and most would speculate maybe a third. Yet these numbers give you just a glimpse of the extent of the problem; unless we begin to address the problem of "disconnectedness," our health care system will become overwhelmed.

I must admit, when Dr. Glasser first asked me to write the forward for a book about fibromyalgia, I actually cringed. "Yikes," I thought. "Not only am I not a rheumatologist, but I have absolutely no idea of where to press on the body to give someone the diagnosis of fibromyalgia. In fact, I rarely even see any of *those* women any more. I used to encounter them quite a bit when I practiced in the suburbs, but now I work in a city, and it seems like I never do. Maybe my patients don't have time for fibromyalgia."

But like many things in my life, my first impressions were wrong. I read and reread Dr. Glasser's book, over and over until it finally sank in: These unhappy women are in pain; isn't that enough? What's the point in getting bogged down in anything more than that?

I began trying to incorporate Dr. Glasser's ideas of Reality Therapy and eventually Choice Theory ever since that sharp pop to my head almost two decades ago. It was an epiphany, of sorts, for me. His principles have helped my family, my friends and me for a long time. And I am absolutely convinced that they can work for you, too, so that instead of being my patients, you can become the happy and fulfilled Janices, Melissas and Davids you want to be... all of whom have simply learned to make better choices.

*****

Dr. Scott Campbell received his B.A. from the University of Michigan with an emphasis in public policy; his M.P.H. from the UCLA School of Public Health with a concentration in behavioral science and health education; and his M.D. from Columbia College of Physicians and Surgeons. He has over ten years of experience as an emergency physician in both the San Francisco Bay Area and Hawaii. He is currently an emergency physician at Kaiser-Permanente in San Francisco.

1

What Is It if It's Not a Disease?

n his article entitled "Hurting All Over" (November 13, 2000 issue of the *New Yorker*)[1] Jerome Groopman M.D., Recanati Professor of Medicine, Harvard Medical School, explains that in the 1970s, one of the first doctors to attempt to define the cluster of symptoms now known as *fibromyalgia* was Frederick Wolfe, Director of the Arthritis Research Center Foundation in Wichita, Kansas. What Dr. Wolfe noted then, and what still remains the most baffling aspect of this disease, is that no pathology has been discovered to explain the rheumatoid-like symptoms. Physical examinations then and now show no evidence of inflammation, subsequent laboratory tests and x-rays are negative, and tissue biopsies fail to show muscle pathology.

In the 1970s there were only a few patients, but by 1987 their numbers had so increased that Dr. Wolfe brought together twenty rheumatologists from the United

States and Canada to codify and try to name the unknown disorder. Three years later in 1990, it was formally named *fibromyalgia* and officially accepted into the medical lexicon as a condition of persistent muscle pain throughout the body, often accompanied by severe fatigue, insomnia, diarrhea, abdominal bloating, bladder irritation, and headache.

Ten years later, in 2000, Dr. Groopman reports that fibromyalgia has become an epidemic. Nearly six million Americans are said to be suffering from it; more than four times as many as will develop cancer this year and six times as many as are living with HIV. Ninety percent of the afflicted are women and the majority are Caucasian. But still no pathology has been found to explain any of the symptoms.

Commenting on this puzzling contradiction, Dr. Groopman states, "The debate over diagnosis and treatment has become so heated it has polarized medical specialists; choosing a doctor has become tantamount to adopting an ideological position." Whatever it is, real to some doctors, imaginary to others, fibromyalgia is by far the most widespread, painful, disabling disease in the United States.

Leading off his article, Dr. Groopman asks the key question, *"With so many people in so much pain, how could fibromyalgia not be a disease?"* With so many women suffering from this disease or whatever it is, there is a desperate need to find an answer to his question. That leads me to the reason I am writing this book and to the title of this chapter: *What is it, if it's not a disease?*

As I read through that fascinating, beautifully written article, I became more and more excited. I believed I could answer both his question and my follow-up question and, in doing so, shed new light on this riddle. In this book I will explain what I believe fibromyalgia is. But I will go far beyond this explanation. I will teach how a sufferer could gain relief from her symptoms. What I teach will build chapter-by-chapter and end with a story that should give hope to everyone with this diagnosis.

To use what I will teach, you do not have to stop or change any present treatment, diet, exercise or medication. If you are involved in counseling, a support group or a self-help practice such as meditation or yoga—literally anything you believe is helping—I encourage you to continue. You are in complete control of how much or how long you use what I will explain. There is no downside. Nothing I teach can possibly do any harm.

While I am a well-known psychiatrist whose theories and practices are taught all over the world, I do not believe you have a psychiatric problem. Of course you're unhappy and depressed, who wouldn't be in your shoes? But just because you are suffering from pain and disability does not make you mentally ill. What you will find out by Chapter Five is that you not only are not psychologically disturbed, you are very likely both a competent and very creative person.

From my personal experience plus the experiences of many of my Institute faculty, I know the ideas can be learned and used in your life. The only problem will be that they are new to you. It takes a while to get used to doing things differently from what you have done for years. But there is no hurry. As much as you are willing to use them they will help you and, eventually, I'm almost certain you will catch on.

From reading Dr. Groopman's article, I know that many of you are taking psychiatric drugs usually prescribed for mental illnesses. Since I don't believe you are mentally ill, I would not prescribe those drugs. But if you are taking them, don't be concerned that their use will interfere with what I teach you to do with your life. Teaching you to live differently, as a cardiologist might teach a sedentary person the value of exercise, is a good analogy to the usefulness and safety of what I suggest you do.

Also, to learn what I will teach, you don't have to sign up for a course, join a group or buy materials. What you need to learn is written in this book and is based on a theory I've been refining for over thirty years, which (since 1996) I've called *Choice Theory*. It is explained in detail in my 1998 book, *Choice Theory: A New Psychology of Personal Freedom*[2].

Based on this theory, I believe that you suffer real pain and real disability. You are not imagining your symptoms. What you do not know, which I will explain, is where your pain is coming from and what you can do to reduce it. This book includes what I believe to be a very user-friendly explanation of Choice Theory. It is also the only material I've written that specifically applies Choice Theory to the symptoms of fibromyalgia.

Choice Theory focuses on the genetic fact that we are as strongly programmed to try to get involved in satisfying relationships as we are to try to find good food to eat or shelter from the cold. Our genes are not only asking that we try to stay alive, they are also concerned that we be happy. But as almost all of us know, it is not easy to find long periods of happiness as we struggle with our lives.

As I will explain, I believe that all symptoms of pain or disability, *for which there is no clear explanation such as in this condition,* have something to do with unhappiness. This does not mean that all unhappy people have symptoms. But it does mean that if you are unhappy, learning how to be happier is a very sensible thing to do. In this book I will teach you to use Choice Theory in your life. If you do, you have a good chance to be happier.

You may also say to me, and many people have, "Dr. Glasser, if I didn't have these symptoms I'd be very happy." I can't argue with that. All I can say is that you have the symptoms and you are unhappy now. And probably nothing you have been doing for the past year or more has helped you. If learning Choice Theory can help you to be happier and also get relief from your symptoms, you'll be much better off than you are now.

If you further ask me, what are the chances of getting rid of my symptoms if I learn Choice Theory and become happier? I'd answer about ten-to-one in your favor or more. This is why I am going to focus on happiness in the rest of this chapter and in the next one. It is the new perspective I mentioned in the title and as you read the rest of this chapter, look at your life before fibromyalgia and see where you fit into what I am now going to explain.

I believe that to be happy, we must figure out how to get along well and connect with the important people in our lives; that is, to connect to the extent we want with friends, spouses, lovers, children, parents, teachers, bosses and coworkers. We don't need to connect with all these people, but to be happy we need to connect strongly with some of them, especially with our marital partner and our children. How many people we need to connect with is up to each one of us, but the absolute minimum for happiness is one strong, satisfying connection.

It takes most people who start to learn Choice Theory a few weeks (or even more) to realize that what I suggest they do as they attempt to connect with the important people in their lives is a radical departure from the way they have dealt with these people and these people have dealt with them in the past. I get many letters saying, "I agree with you, your ideas make sense, but it's hard to change what I've done for so long. I keep slipping back into my old ways."

Please, don't be discouraged. What the people who write me are complaining about is not what I'm trying to teach; they all say they like the ideas. It's the same problem you've had all your life when you try to break a habit. It just takes a little concentration. What will motivate you to break this habit more than others you've tried to break, is the more you use Choice Theory in your life, the better you should feel.

Learning Choice Theory takes effort. But, by the end of the fourth chapter of this book, I believe you will have learned enough to be able to understand why you can't separate many of the ways you presently think and act from your pain or other symptoms; they are branches of the same tree. But to some extent, you already know this. If you work for a boss like Ebenezer Scrooge and suffer from headaches, you know there is nothing medically wrong with you. Your headaches disappear over the weekend and start again Monday on the way to work.

This Scrooge you work for needs a visit from a ghost who will teach him that you are a human being with feelings who, for happiness and health, needs to be connected with him and others with whom you work. These ghosts are hard to come by but, fortunately, Choice Theory is not. Your boss may not change but Choice Theory will teach you how to deal with him without feeling as if your head is about to split.

Less then half the people in the country stay in their first marriages over ten years. But even if you have, as many of you surely know, that does not mean that you are happy. A lifelong, happy marriage is a rare event indeed, even for people who seem able to get along well with almost everyone else in their life. There is nothing abnormal about not getting along with your mate as well as you'd like since the world we live in is not a Choice Theory world. If it were, we'd all be a lot happier.

What this book will teach you is how to depend on yourself for happiness. When you do, you will immediately begin to get along better with people whom you are having trouble getting along with now.

For years I have noticed two situations that I am sure many of you have also observed. First, anyone in an unsatisfying relationship with someone he or she wants very much to get along better with is unhappy. Second, even without fibromyalgia, most of these unhappy people suffer from one or more painful symptoms such as: headache, backache, depression, anxiety, fatigue, insomnia, or upset stomach, with headache and backache being the most common.

What I will teach you is why so many people are unhappy. I will also teach you specific things you can do that will help you find the happiness you need. Also, even though you are suffering from all the symptoms that are now recognized as fibromyalgia, I'm not in any way intimating that you are inadequate or even hard to get along with. Actually, I believe that if we had a chance to meet, it is very likely I'd find you to be a pleasure to get to know.

What I am saying here is that there are new ideas you should consider learning to use in your life. These ideas should help you get relief from your symptoms by teaching you how to connect more effectively with the important people in your life. The title of this book, *Hope from a Completely New Perspective*, is honest. Choice Theory is the new perspective.

2

Happiness and Unhappiness

K aren, a forty-two-year-old, slightly overweight, young-looking, attractive woman, is sitting comfortably in my office chatting. I'd been looking for a woman with fibromyalgia and I got her name from a friend of hers who got her permission to give it to me. I called and told her I became interested in this disease because of an article I'd read in the *New Yorker* and she told me she'd read the same article. I asked her what she thought of it and she said it was very accurate. Her doctor had told her from the start that he had no explanation or treatment for her pain.

On the phone, I told her I was convinced that her pain was real; there was nothing imaginary about it. But I had an idea about where the pain was coming from and I wanted someone to test my ideas on. I explained that I wasn't interested in the details of the disease itself and had no specific treatment to offer. What I was curious about were the relationships of the women who have been suffering with it. I felt there might be some connection between their relationships and the pain. She agreed to come in when I assured her there'd be no pressure on her to do anything more than listen to my questions and, if she were comfortable, answer them.

I asked her if getting here was difficult. She said it was par for the course—painful—but no more painful than it usually was to drive the car. I then said, "Anyway, now that you're here, all you have to do is relax and talk. Take your time. With all the pain and discomfort you're having, if it takes a moment or two to concentrate, take it." She told me she was fine and asked what I wanted to know. So I began by asking, "Would you tell me about a time since you became an adult, but before you were diagnosed, when you were very happy?"

She hardly hesitated and said, "It was when I was twenty-two. I fell in love with Gary, the man who's now my husband. I'd had a few relationships but this was different. The sex was glorious, much better than I'd ever had. In no time, I was deeply in love. I was living with a girlfriend who taught school. When I found out who you were, I recognized your name immediately. My roommate had a couple of your books on our bookshelf. Anyway, I'd taken a job in a department store as an assistant buyer and I was surprised at how much I enjoyed the work. Carol, my roommate, was also in love with a man. I can't tell you how happy we were and the four of us all got along so well. Gary was in dental school when we got engaged and I loved the idea of being married to a professional man. My family was mostly blue collar. We were so in love we didn't want to be apart any more than we had to be so we decided to get married. The deal was I'd support him until he finished school and got his practice started. Once he could see that all his loans were under control, I could keep working or quit. I liked the job and worked after I could have quit—actually, until our first child was in school and our second was out of diapers. Those eight years between the time we fell in love and when he got his office going were the happiest years of my life."

We talked a while more about those happy years, and what she stressed over and over was that even though they were poor and struggling, she felt so loved and appreciated that having so little money made no difference. Even the temporary poverty was romantic because they could see their life was on the right track and believed things could only get better as he succeeded. What they had was each other; it seemed to be all they needed.

Then I asked the opposite question and told her she didn't have to answer if she didn't want to. "Before you were diagnosed, but after you were married, what was the most unhappy time in your life?"

She thought for about twenty seconds and then said, "It wasn't really that way. Like I was suddenly unhappy because something terrible happened. Nothing terrible has ever happened—well, I mean, until five years ago when I got sick. I guess the best way you could put it is our happiness just slipped away. We seemed to need each other less and less. It was like he had his life and I had my mine but our life together—the really happy life together—disappeared. But no big unhappiness, no separations, neither of us ever thought about divorce, nothing like so many of our friends have been through; even my friend Carol is now divorced. We had sex, we still have—not often—but it seems enough. But it's different from what it used to be.

Now, the sex is more for our own personal pleasure than for each other's. Do you see what I'm trying to tell you?"

"I do. It's the story of a lot of women in their forties who are married to successful men, not really unhappy but not happy either. Do you ever think about trying to do something to get some of the old feelings back?"

There was a pause. My guess was she was thinking about what she'd felt like when she was happy. Then she said, "I try not to. What's the point? Things aren't going to change. We still have a lot more going for us than many of our friends. In our crowd, ours is considered one of the good marriages."

"So what's really not so great about it?"

"We get on each other's nerves. Little things, picking on each other, taking a moment longer to answer than is necessary. Just like everything in the beginning was right, now nothing seems to be right. If things are kind of okay, it's a good day."

I just looked at her and she went on, "Where we used to be sweet and considerate, now we're sour and inconsiderate. Again, no big deal, it's just never very good. We spend a lot of time asking, 'Why can't you be like you used to be?' But don't get me wrong, it's no big deal, it's just irritating."

"Do either of you ever ask yourselves, 'Why can't I be like I used to be?' "

"That's a new idea, maybe I ought to try it. Then how do you get him to try it? I just can't up and ask him."

"What's happened since the diagnosis?"

"The disease has changed things a lot. He's interested in me again or I guess you could say he's more interested in the sick me than he was in the healthy me. But then I think to myself, 'Do I have to be suffering to get his attention?' Still, I like it and I do my best to be healthy. I don't talk much about the pain and try to live as normal a life as I can. But I have some really bad days and I can't hide them. This disease has a lot of ups and downs."

"Do you know when it's going to go up or down?"

"That's it, I don't. It just seems to happen. It doesn't seem to be related to anything."

"Do you spend a lot of time going from doctor to doctor for help?"

"I did for the first three years, not so much now. I still go for my exams but I wait longer in between. What I now have is an exercise program that seems to keep me limber. I think I'm getting a little stronger."

"This has been going on a long time. I wonder, are you still hoping for a cure like a new medication or a treatment program that's going to really change things?"

"They keep telling me that they can't really find anything wrong. That's both encouraging and discouraging. I'm not crippled up like some people with arthritis but I'm discouraged because no one really seems to know what's wrong. I hurt, but look at me. Just to see me sitting here, I don't even look sick. When I ask if I'm ever going to get better, I don't really get any answers. I still read all the new stuff. To tell you the truth, I came because you're a doctor. I'll admit I was a little disappointed when you told me coming here wasn't about treatment. But then I realized you're a psychiatrist and all you do is talk. So I figured, why not talk to him? God knows I need something besides the 'you-again' looks I get when I show up for my appointments. But I can't blame them. This screwy disease gets everyone down."

"I'm not talking to you as a psychiatrist, I told you that on the phone."

"I know, but I didn't believe you. It's okay, I'm enjoying being here."

"Karen, I'm talking with you in hopes that I'll be able to offer you something. Not just you, but anyone with this disease. Something that you may be able to use to help yourself. Do these questions I've asked you mean anything in particular?"

"I'm kind of glad you don't want to hear about the sickness. I wish I could stop thinking about myself and asking over and over, 'Why me?' I'm tired of thinking about myself. That's not the kind of person I am. But the questions—you know, the ones about happiness and unhappiness—I guess you're trying to make a connection between my pain and my unhappiness. You are, aren't you?"

"I am. I think there is a connection."

"I hate to disappoint you, but I can't really accept that the little unhappiness I've had in my marriage could even come close to causing this much pain. It just doesn't add up in my mind. I mean, I hurt all over. I'm tired and I'm depressed. I haven't been happy for a long time. If it has to do with unhappiness, why did it take so long to happen? And then the other thing—all this pain—and they tell me nothing's wrong. How could I feel like this and nothing be wrong?"

"I'm trying to answer that question. I think something is wrong but it's hard to explain. Every time I think I'm ready to explain it, I stop because I think I'm going to be misunderstood, and that could make things worse. I'm working on it and I think I'll get it. But before I say anything more, do you trust me when I tell you I think all your symptoms are real? Pain is pain. It's not imaginary. What I'm hoping is if I get to the point where I can explain what's on my mind without being misunderstood, you'll trust me enough to try what I suggest. This thing I'm working on is a do-it-yourself program. I teach it; you put it into practice."

"I don't know. I'm not sure I trust anyone where this disease is concerned. I've seen psychiatrists, two of them. They asked me about my childhood, my parents and my marriage. They asked me about my pain and my other symptoms. One asked a lot about my sex life. I mean, it was okay. They were trying to help me, but their questions didn't seem to get anywhere. They both asked the same questions, except for the sex part, and I gave them the same answers. Then they both offered to give me psychiatric drugs like I was mentally ill. I even took some Prozac for awhile. It didn't help. And I'm not mentally ill. Do I sound like I'm mentally ill to you?" I shook my head no and she went on. "They both told me I'm depressed as if this should be news to me. Of course, I'm depressed. How could I not be? I hurt all the time. I can't lead a normal life. On some days I can't even drive the car. And now, your question about happiness—believe me, if I didn't have this disease, I'd be happy right now."

"I'm sure you would be. But the fact is you've had the disease for close to five years. And I don't think you've heard anything new about it since the start. I'm going to offer you something new. I'm just hoping you'll trust me enough to take seriously what I think I'm going to come up with."

"Don't worry. I'll take what you suggest seriously whether I trust you or not. And look, I'm not asking for a cure. Help me to feel better for a few weeks and I'll be grateful. You have no idea what I go through every day, you really don't."

"Okay, I'm going to try. I should be able to come up with something in a couple of months. I really appreciate your spending this time with me. You've probably been hurting since we started to talk and not one complaint."

"I try not to complain but I haven't hurt that much since we've been talking. Like I said, the pain comes and goes. It's nothing now but on the way home I may pay for this little respite."

"I'm thinking about writing a book on fibromyalgia. I may need some more help after I organize my thoughts. I'd like to send you some chapters for your comments. Would that be okay?"

"Sure, I'll help. I've read a lot of stuff but no one's ever asked me for help. I like that idea. Do you really think you'll have something in a couple of months?"

"I'm ready to start. I don't think it'll take very long. It'll be a short book. But something's just occurred to me. Would it be okay if I put what we've talked about today in it? I'll disguise you; no one but you will ever know."

"You don't have to disguise me. If what you write is just what we talked about, there'd be no problem. I'd like to help. I don't consider myself a helpless person and this pain makes me feel so insignificant. I appreciate your asking me to talk with you. I'll look forward to hearing from you."

Karen left my office in a good mood. A few days later I began writing. After I wrote the first chapter and the interview with Karen that begins this chapter, I continued by comparing happiness and unhappiness.

Happiness

If you think back into your adult life as Karen did, I believe you'll find that you were the happiest when, like

Karen, you were in an intimate relationship in which you were cared for and respected. In most instances you were so satisfied you didn't think much about your relationship because you were confident that if a problem came up, it could be easily solved. You loved each other. As long as you have a lot of it, love can conquer all.

But very satisfying relationships do not have to be intimate. Children who love and respect us and live lives we can be proud of are possibly the greatest source of lifelong happiness. Good friends and colleagues at work keep many of us happy even when our intimate relationships leave much to be desired.

Happiness can come with sharing intellectual and artistic experiences, from traveling, and expanding our horizons in all directions as long as we are able to do it with people we care for and respect. You can be content, even satisfied, when you are alone but not for very long. None of us can be happy when we're lonely.

Unhappiness

Simplistic as it may sound, I believe the basic human problem is unhappiness. Excluding grinding poverty, incurable disease, and living under tyranny, essentially all human unhappiness is caused by our inability to get along the way we would like with the important people in our lives. I believe that fibromyalgia has no pathology because it's not a disease. It is an unwanted side effect of some of the behaviors we choose when we are unhappy. For example, when we are lonely we really don't want to be depressed. It is one of those unwanted side effects.

Remember when Karen said, "Of course, I am depressed. How could I not be? I hurt all the time. I can't lead a normal life." She was saying that when she was suffering all the pain of fibromyalgia. It's normal to have the additional pain and suffering of what is commonly called depression. But everyone in the world knows that you don't have to be suffering from fibromyalgia to be depressed. It's actually the most common pain and suffering that we all feel whenever our life is not going the way we want, which is another way of saying we're unhappy.

But before she said she was depressed she told me, "I'm not mentally ill. Do I sound like I'm mentally ill to you?" Karen is not mentally ill. She's suffering emotionally and physically at the same time. In my opinion, suffering is not the criterion for mental illness. The criterion for mental illness is the same as the criterion for physical illness: the presence of pathology.

Alzheimer's disease is a mental illness because the brain is riddled with lesions. Rheumatoid arthritis is a physical illness for the reason that the joints of the body are being destroyed by inflammation. As much as it is labeled a mental illness, depression has no pathology and is something else. Although fibromyalgia by its symptoms seems to be a physical illness, it has no pathology and therefore is also something else.

That something else—depression, fibromyalgia, chronic-fatigue syndrome, or any one of several hundred other conditions—is associated with, but not caused by, unhappiness. In Chapter Four I will explain in detail what that something else is.

In the spring of 2000, Dr. Groopman described a gathering of more than 750 Caucasian women, between the ages of twenty and sixty, all crowded into the grand ballroom of the Westin Hotel just outside of Boston. He painted a vivid picture of their arrival: "Some walked with canes that had a four-point base, others wore braces on their wrists and ankles, and many limped."

They were attending a seminar on fibromyalgia sponsored by the pharmaceutical companies that make the psychiatric medications often prescribed for this condition. All the women were there, hoping to get relief from their pain and disability. They were not there because they thought they were mentally ill.

It is my belief that essentially all of them were unhappy prior to the onset of their fibromyalgia even though now, with their pain and disability, very few of them had much recollection of how unsatisfying a major relationship in their lives may have been. I'm sure most of them would say like Karen did, "Believe me, if I didn't have this disease, I'd be happy right now."

One thing certain about this painful condition is that once it is in full flower, as it was with the women at the Westin Hotel, it impedes their ability to make much of a contribution to the important relationships in their lives.

This becomes the start of a vicious cycle. Even though they may be unhappy, their contributions to their relationships with their husbands and families are as much needed as ever. But now with their pain, weakness and fatigue, they are unable to do as much for others as they used to. This inability further harms their relationships, the symptoms increase and they get to the point where these symptoms literally take over their lives. Now all they can think of is they need someone or something to get rid of the symptoms.

I believe that by the time they gathered in the Westin, most of them had all but given up on the idea that they could help themselves. This book is my attempt to persuade you to learn something new that you can use to help yourself and contribute more to your relationships. This can lead to more happiness and less symptoms, literally reversing the vicious cycle. Hypothetically, as your happiness increases, your ability to deal with your relationships increases, while your pain decreases. But what I will also explain later in this book is what went wrong with relationships in the first place and how you can correct them. I feel certain they still need correcting.

Later when I explain what went wrong with your relationships I think it will show that the precipitating unhappiness for fibromyalgia is more like what Karen described, a growing feeling that the good relationship you had was now slowly disappearing, rather than a sudden disruption in your life. You became more and more aware that your life was not working out nearly the way you wanted but you seemed helpless to do much about it.

But slow or fast, the unhappiness was, and very likely still is, your inability to get along with the important people in your life the way you want. It might be good to stop now and ask yourself the two questions I asked Karen: *when were you happy and when were you unhappy?* If you answer them truthfully, I think your answer will be very much like hers and you will begin to see that there was a big difference between the life you once had and the life you were living prior to the onset of the fibromyalgia.

Also, when I asked Karen about her unhappiness before the onset of her disease, she told me that her marital disappointment was nothing compared to the increase in unhappiness after the disease became established. When you are in severe physical pain, all you think about is your pain and the life you are forced to lead because of it. Your previous pain-free unhappiness seems almost inconsequential. But I don't believe it was inconsequential. It was enough to start the process that accelerated into the vicious cycle that led to where you are now.

The reason there are so many unhappy people is that we are social creatures, we need each other and we don't do well by ourselves. Yet huge numbers of us are unable to maintain long-term, happy relationships, as Karen was unable to do. Our language is peppered with words like *lonely, rejected, isolated, separated, disconnected, forsaken, and desolate* and all are strongly associated with unhappy relationships.

In these days of managed care where doctor-patient time is measured in minutes, there is little chance for your doctor to get to know you, much less to build the supportive relationship with you that, in this diagnosis, you may very much need. In fact, your doctor and other medical personnel having less time to get to know you may be more the rule than the exception.

Many doctors think that giving you more time and attention may also be harmful. They don't come right out and say it but they intimate that your symptoms are more a cry for help than a disease. In a sense, I believe they are right but I also understand their frustration; they are puzzled. They have no awareness that your medical symptoms may be associated with unhappy relationships and if they did have this awareness, they would have no way to treat it. Dr. Groopman addresses this issue by saying:

> Careless and disparaging language [from medical personnel] can certainly alienate patients who are in desperate need of care, and yet opponents of the current treatment of fibromyalgia say that unquestioning acceptance of the condition may

be equally harmful. Some, like Dr. Thomas Bohr, a neurologist at Loma Linda School of Medicine, in California, and Dr. Arthur Barsky, a professor of Psychiatry at Harvard, contend that even honoring this bundle of symptoms with a medical label may be doing more to make people sick than to cure them. These doctors don't claim that the symptoms of fibromyalgia are not real, only that their origin lies in the mind and not in the peripheral nerves of the body.

I certainly agree with this, but I ask, what difference does it make to you where the pain originates? Whether the cause is in your peripheral nerves or in your mind, you are still in pain and want relief. If the pain is a tangible component of the unhappiness associated with an unsatisfying relationship, it does no good to worry about where it originates.

What you need are things you can do, even with your fibromyalgia, that can help you solve your relationship problems and be happier than you are now. At the end of this book, I will encourage you to test my suggestions.

What rarely happens when a sufferer of fibromyalgia visits a doctor's office long enough to have the diagnosis established is to have a doctor offer the following, "Look, for the time being I've done all I can do. I have to admit that no one understands your condition but there's no hurry today. Why don't we take twenty minutes and let me try to get to know you as an intelligent, sensitive woman, not just as a suffering patient?"

I welcomed this kind of intervention some years ago when I was sixty-two. Suddenly I became ill with a life-threatening symptom. It happened first while I was playing tennis but then continued on and off for about three years, sometimes after exertion, sometimes not. With no warning, my heart would start beating 275 to 300 times a minute. The first time it happened it went on for four hours before I could get to a distant hospital. My doctor later told me this was about the best stress test you could go through and commented, "If your heart could withstand that, there couldn't be very much wrong with it."

And there wasn't. Even though these attacks of what they called supraventricular tachycardia continued, no pathology was ever found. I had about fifteen episodes, all very frightening. Sometimes my heart converted on its own but at least eight times I had to have it shocked back to a normal rhythm. After exhaustive tests, the doctor I finally settled on told me honestly that there was nothing he could find wrong with my heart. This was after I'd had an episode in the hospital immediately following a six-hour test during which they probed around inside my heart and found nothing.

To say I was unhappy is putting it mildly. Like I said, my doctor was honest. After about the tenth time I saw him, he had no difficulty admitting he couldn't help and even though he gave me some medicine, he told me that while it might not do any good, it probably wouldn't harm me.

Then, with no apparent need to hurry, he asked me if I had any idea why this was happening. Was there anything going on in my life that might have something to do with this condition? It wasn't that I expected him to do anything no matter how I answered this question. It was the fact that he *asked* me, *listened* to me, and gave me the impression that he believed my heart problem could be connected with some things that were going on in my life. That impression gave me hope. I could do something about that.

I felt very comfortable telling him that there were things happening in my life that might have a lot to do with my heart and I was working to solve them. I even shared one with him. He listened with interest but made no comment except to nod when I said I was working on them. His interest encouraged me to keep thinking and finally, to change some things in my life. When I did, the episodes stopped and I slowly tapered off the medication. I can't prove that what I figured out is what stopped them but I firmly believe it was. Now ten years later, I've had no recurrence but I've continued to live my life differently.

What I figured out is similar to what I will explain in this book. Like my doctor, I will strongly encourage you to use what I suggest to help yourself. I don't know what the actual unhappiness in your life is and I don't believe it has to be a very sizable unhappiness. But whatever it is, it's the kind of thing you believe you ought to be able to solve but somehow you can't seem to solve it. And it rankles you.

For the six million women like you, your major relationship problem is almost always restricted to a small group of people with whom you were once happy. Specifically, this is a husband, an ex-husband, a man friend, or a man you are having or had been having an affair with. Women tend to wear their hearts on their sleeves and the amount of unhappiness you suffered or are still suffering is usually proportional to how happy you once were with this person. The happier you were, the unhappier you are when the relationship fails.

The next group, considerable but not as large, is first your children and then your grandchildren. Huge numbers of middle-aged women are being drained by the care of what is often a troublesome grandchild or grandchildren. After this group comes your parents, especially demanding, elderly parents who are expert at intimating you should be doing more for them. Next come members of your family, especially your brothers and sisters, or even cousins, aunts, uncles, or grandparents. Then there are very close friends you may have had a major falling out with. Finally, there are people at work. It can be a boss, a co-worker, or even a subordinate who treats you in a way that you dread going to work.

If your fibromyalgia is associated with unhappiness, the people just mentioned are the ones you will need to consider dealing with differently. If there are other people besides these, the same thing applies. Your task, unfair as it may seem to you, will be to change your behavior, not spend your time and effort trying to change them. If you could change them, it's unlikely you'd have the problem to begin with.

3

The Genetic Needs

When we are born, we don't know very much about what's going on. But very quickly we begin to learn a lot. It's surprising how much a three-month-old baby knows and is able to do. The driving force behind this learning and what we are able to do with it is our feelings. As an adult, most of the time we don't think much about them. But there are times when our feelings get so strong they dominate our lives.

For example, a talented young actor addicted to drugs has been in and out of the newspaper for years. In his quest to experience the highs of addicting drugs, he is, in my opinion, throwing his life away. In sharp contrast but equally driven by their feelings, are the women who gathered at the Westin Hotel. Their lives were driven by their desire to rid themselves of pain. The actor would be well off if he could settle for less pleasure. The women won't be well off until they get relief from their pain.

Starting at birth, we begin to work individually to figure out how much pleasure it is reasonable to expect and how much effort we should exert to avoid pain. There are, however, huge differences in how individuals work this out. The almost infinite variety of behaviors we choose as we search for pleasure and try to avoid pain are all driven by five basic needs encoded in our genes. It is these needs that give purpose to our behavior.

These genetic needs are *survival, love and belonging, power, freedom, and fun.* As varied as the needs are, only one need-satisfying behavior—anger—is encoded in our genes. All the other many thousands of behaviors that we use as we attempt to satisfy our needs are learned. Everything we choose to do from birth to death is driven by our desire to experience the pleasure of satisfying one or more of these needs or to avoid the pain of not satisfying one or more of them.

A newborn baby doesn't know about food or care. But she knows how she feels, at least the difference between how she felt in the womb and how she feels now. Almost immediately she will forget about how she felt in the womb and pay attention to how she feels as she goes about trying to satisfy her five needs. All of our lives we will know how we feel more accurately than anything else we experience.

Fortunately, the newborn has been given anger to help get the process started. She can cry, scream, fuss, and in some way express what seems to be anger at her discomfort with the birth process and how she feels now. Almost always there is a caring person who pays attention to her discomfort and helps her to satisfy her needs, at first mostly survival, but then love. If she is fed but not held or cuddled, she will soon give up trying to get attention, go into what seems like a depression and die. This death from insufficient love and attention has been recognized as a disease and labeled *marasmus*. This disease illustrates how strongly we need relationships starting at birth.

By the time she is several months old she has learned a variety of need-satisfying behaviors, both to avoid pain and experience pleasure. She will add to and subtract from this behavioral warehouse for the rest of her life as she goes about the immediate business of satisfying her needs. She screams for food when she feels hunger pangs and learns to enjoy the pleasure of eating. She demands attention when she wants love and learns the pleasure of being loved and of loving back.

She gets an early taste of the pleasure of power when she sees people jump to attend to her when she screams. Later she learns not to demand too much as she'll be setting herself up for a lot of frustration. There are times when she'd like to play with her cradle toys and learn how to manipulate them and she'll scream for the freedom to be left alone to do this. As she explores her environment and learns, she begins to satisfy her need for fun and the pleasure that goes with satisfying it. I believe this fun is the genetic reward for learning something new, interesting, and most often useful.

If you want to check out what I've just explained, just keep track of your different behaviors for a day or two and you will notice that much of what you do satisfies more than one need. For example, after I read Dr. Groopman's article I was driven to write this book by the potential pleasure of satisfying four of my five needs: love, power, freedom, and fun. In the life I lead, survival has little to do with my motivation.

I chose to be a psychiatrist because I care for people, and this book is certainly driven by love. I feel your pain and I want to do all I can to help you overcome it. I am driven by my need for power and the possible recognition I will get if these ideas prove useful not only for fibromyalgia but for many other conditions that I believe are now mistakenly called diseases, such as depression. I am not driven by lack of freedom; I feel fortunate that I have the freedom to devote a lot of time to this project. Since I began it, I have learned a great deal more about Choice Theory. My need for fun is satisfied as I continue to work on this book.

As much as we are driven by the pleasure of satisfying our needs, unfortunately, that same pleasure can be our undoing. The young actor I mentioned is well into the process of destroying his life with drugs. The problem with addiction is that the drug mimics the pleasure of actually satisfying a need and may produce more sure, quick pleasure than any normal, need-satisfying activity could possibly produce. But the drug cannot provide happiness. That is a pleasure that can only be experienced if we can satisfy our need for love and belonging. Because it requires the cooperation of someone else, it is the most difficult need for all of us to satisfy.

For example, almost all of us are addicted to eating. If we can't get food, we suffer. But if you give opium to a starving child, as they did to stop the hunger pangs of children in nineteenth-century England, you fool the brain into thinking the survival need for food has been satisfied. Many of you, suffering from the pain of fibromyalgia, are taking drugs. But the problem with any drug that relieves pain is that it is addictive and over time any addiction deprives the addict of the love and belonging his/her genes need for happiness. This is why drugs, as Dr. Groopman noted in his article, are generally unsuccessful for this condition.

When talking about her early happiness in her marriage, Karen described her feelings as ecstatic at times. She was more than able to satisfy her need for love and belonging in that relationship. Then as a couple, she and her husband's need for power was also satisfied. They both felt appreciated and respected. No one likes to be controlled. To satisfy both love and power in a locked-together relationship such as marriage is a challenge that many of us have yet to figure out.

Marital power struggles such as husbands beating wives, is the source of much of the violence in this country. Marriage, childcare, and the care of elderly parents can also create marital and family conflicts because so much freedom has to be given up. But there is also the other side of the coin. Karen probably had more freedom in her less-than-happy relationship than she wanted.

Learning how to keep love alive and still have some freedom is a challenge both to marriage and parenting that is not well solved by many couples. Fun is probably more important to successful relationships than most people realize. Couples who keep learning together share the happiest marriages. A couple or family who stop learning has little to keep them together. How to use Choice Theory to deal with all these frustrating situations and keep the relationships strong will be covered in the final chapters of this book.

To get back to the women assembled at the Westin, I believe many of them for years had been unable to satisfy their needs enough to be happy in one or more of their important relationships. That frustration was at the genetic level. For as long as we are alive, our needs will push for satisfaction. We may try, but we can not turn them off. We can fool our needs with addicting drugs, but neither the women in that ballroom nor their doctors want to use those drugs. Becoming addicted is hardly the answer.

Before I go further, let me say something that may give you a little food for thought. Suppose as soon as you finish this book, but before you put any of what I'm going to suggest into practice, medical researchers discover that your fibromyalgia is caused by a defective gene similar to the recent discovery that the cause of some cancers is genetic. You might call me up on the phone and say, "Here it is in black and white in today's health section of the newspaper. It says that fibromyalgia is caused by two defective genes in the sixteenth chromosome. You're wrong to claim it's associated with my unhappiness."

First of all I'd say, "Now that they've discovered the genes, what help are they offering? Do they have replacement genes they can insert into your body and cure your disease?"

Because genetic cures are a way down the road, you might answer, "No, they're a long way from a cure but at least they know what it is and where to focus their research."

I'd say, "Are you going to suffer any less because they found the cause, if no relief is in sight?"

You might then answer, "Well, now that they know what the cause is, maybe they will find a cure. But at least I won't have to put up with your idea that my unhappiness is a part of this misery. Most of the people I know are not as happy now as they were when they fell in love but they don't have fibromyalgia."

I hope that's an accurate reflection of what would be on your mind. But suppose no cause is found. Things remain as Dr. Groopman explained in the article and you're going to suffer for years, maybe for the rest of your life. Remember, fibromyalgia is a disease without a pathology. Until that pathology is found, medical doctors treating it are going to use the same shotgun approach—a little here and a little there—that they have been using since it was accepted as a disease.

But if you're choosing the pain *indirectly,* I will be able to teach you—not counsel you, not medicate you, but teach you—why and how to make some new, and completely safe, choices in your life that may give you some relief. You know what choices you have now. I'm offering you one that is very likely different from any you've been offered so far. It is, however, a choice that cannot possibly harm you.

4

Total Behavior and Creativity

W hen I attempt to explain how the pain and fatigue of fibromyalgia can occur without supportive pathology, I think about driving in Germany on the autobahn in 1994. I had a medium-size rental car and was having difficulty getting out of the way of the big Mercedes and BMWs that were cruising past me very comfortably at 120 mph. At 100 mph, my car began to shake and sputter but when I slowed down to 90 mph, it corrected itself and ran well. I realized the problem was not a mechanical failure. It occurred because I was asking more from the car than it was capable of delivering. I believe this is a good analogy for fibromyalgia.

In this chapter I will explain that the symptoms of fibromyalgia are not caused by cellular pathology. They are an *unwanted* part of an ineffective behavior you are presently choosing as you try to deal with your unhappiness. But for this claim to make sense to you, I need to teach you that *Choice Theory explains that all we do from birth to death is behave, that all our behaviors are total behaviors, and that all our total behaviors are chosen.* It is this choosing concept that gives Choice Theory its name.

The power of this concept is this: there is nothing to prevent you from choosing different total behaviors from the ones you are choosing now. If you are unhappy, as I believe you are, you can choose more effective total behaviors that do not include the parts you don't want, the parts that are painful and disabling. The goal of this book is to teach you enough Choice Theory so you can learn to choose these more effective total behaviors.

Total Behavior

Ordinarily, most people don't think much about the word *behavior*. It's something we usually take for granted, as we behave every day of our lives. If we think about behavior at all, we consider it a *single activity* that we can choose to change or correct without too much trouble.

It rarely occurs to anyone, and certainly it has never occurred to Karen, that the behavior she's choosing day after day to deal with her husband may be the indirect source of her suffering. Of course, there is no way for Karen to know that her behavior is as complicated as I will now begin to explain. Behavior is far more than a single entity; it is a total of *four very different but inseparable components* that Choice Theory teaches are best called *total behavior*.

Two of these components, your *thinking* and *acting*, are essentially *under your direct control*. You choose what you think about and how you act as you are choosing to read and think about this page. The other two, your *feelings* and *physiology*, *are not under your direct control*.

If you like what you are reading, you will feel good but your physiology will remain about the same. If, however, you suddenly see a fire engine pull up to your house with its siren blasting, your heart may start to beat rapidly.

While you can't control your feelings and your physi-+ology directly, *you can gain a lot of control over them indirectly by changing the way you think and act*. For example, you can't just choose to feel good or choose to increase your heart rate. If you suffer from fibromyalgia, you can't directly choose to stop the pain or get rid of the fatigue. But if you can learn to think and act more effectively, I believe your symptoms will start to disappear. Exactly, how this can happen will be explained in Chapters Six, Seven and Eight.

I realize the idea that extreme pain may be a component of what we commonly choose to do may seem so farfetched it is almost beyond belief. But fibromyalgia is a farfetched condition. Millions of people, mostly middle- and upper-middle-class Caucasian women suffer from it. And so far, no one has been able to explain the cause of their pain and why it attacks this usually healthy group.

I also think it is safe to say that as long as its origin remains unknown, there is little chance that anyone will discover a consistent way to reduce or eliminate its symptoms. In this chapter, I will explain that once you understand total behavior, fibromyalgia will seem much less mysterious and there is a good chance you could help yourself. All our behaviors are total behaviors, but for the sake of brevity in the material that follows, I may not always insert *total* in front of the word *behavior*.

The Complications Involved in Trying to Satisfy Our Need for Love

Assuming we are not hungry, cold, or in danger, I think we pay more attention to how we feel when we are trying to satisfy our need for love than any other situation in our lives. Almost all the world's literature, movies, theater, opera, and even art, focus on the feelings associated with love, especially when the love is in trouble. I'd like to focus on how we behave when we try to satisfy this need.

A good way to conceptualize your life is to think of yourself as a four-wheel-drive car. You are driven by a five-cylinder engine with each cylinder representing one of the five genetic needs: survival, love and belonging, power, freedom, and fun. The engine, therefore, is your complete motivation.

The front wheels, acting and thinking, work together and steer your life in the most need-satisfying direction you can figure out. It is obvious this is not an easy task and we often steer our lives down some very bumpy roads. The rear wheels, feeling and physiology, always follow the front wheels and give us a lot of information about how bumpy the road is. Fibromyalgia, which is made up of a lot of pain and physiologic discomfort, is a very bumpy road to drive on.

When Karen's marriage began to deteriorate no one at that point could predict how much pain or what kind of pain or physiologic discomfort she would experience. But that she would feel pain and/or discomfort was totally predictable. In Karen's case, we know that she turned onto the road of fibromyalgia and has been driving on that road for five years. As she explained, that road for her also contained the potholes of depression.

What is so different from the road of fibromyalgia than from other painful roads (such as the more common road of depression) is that in fibromyalgia your *physiology* almost always gets involved. The abdominal bloating, diarrhea, bladder irritation and fatigue that accompany your muscle pain are the physiological components.

Both her feelings and her physiology would improve if she could learn to act and think in ways that would improve her marriage. She could choose to try to salvage it or to give up on it and look for a more satisfying relationship. As long as she chose to do nothing, she would continue on that road. Our genetic needs will not allow us to accept long-term need frustration without letting us know about it through one or both of our rear wheels.

There is, however, no way to predict how much pain or how much physiologic discomfort we will have when we try to live with less love than we want. Another woman in an unhappy marriage might have little pain or only slight discomfort. The only thing that would always be the same for both of them is neither would consider themselves happy. Further, while both of them are unhappy, neither of them is sick. If either of them could find a way to behave that would improve their current relationships, they would begin to steer their lives down a much more satisfying road and move from unhappy to happy. So far no one knows exactly why one woman may just have a little discomfort while Karen has fibromyalgia. But I think it is safe to say that, for reasons peculiar to her, Karen is much unhappier in her marriage.

There may be fifty million women in the country who are in unhappy relationships, but this book is specifically addressed to the Karens in that group. Still, everything in it can help every woman who is trying to find love. All unhappy women want better relationships and in their own way, they are all suffering.

Now I want to explain what puzzled Karen when she told me that she wasn't doing anything extreme in her marriage. She said they didn't fight but that the happiness just wasn't there anymore. To explain how very ordinary, even appropriate, total behaviors can lead to a lot of misery, I'd like you to consider Ellen, recently diagnosed with fibromyalgia.

Ellen is the single mother of Samantha, a fifteen-year-old who has lost interest in school and does little more than socialize. All she wants to do every weekend is party with an older crowd who drinks, uses drugs and is into sex. Ellen is not imagining this. Samantha tells her what's going on but she assures Ellen that she's cool, not to worry.

But Ellen does worry, as does every mother of a fifteen-year-old like Samantha. Like many mothers, Ellen is on her own. Samantha's father has remarried and has a new family. He offers vocal support when she calls him but nothing more. Ellen finally decides to use the total behavior of *grounding* Samantha if she's not home by eleven on Saturday nights. This has resulted in Samantha being grounded at least every other weekend.

The direct or chosen components of grounding Samantha are Ellen's *thinking*, "I'm worried about her," and her *actions* of keeping Samantha in the house on weekends. This choice traps Ellen in the house all weekend with a surly, abusive teenager who has no mercy for her mother or her fibromyalgia. Samantha doesn't accept Ellen's reasoning that she's protecting Samantha from herself. Since she grounded Samantha, Ellen is even more miserable than she was before the grounding. She has no adult who cares about her and what love is left in her relationship with Samantha is disappearing fast.

Ellen's action to ground Samantha is supported by her belief that she is choosing to do the right thing. Samantha's father supports that belief but offers no tangible help. As this continues, the *feeling* part of Ellen's chosen total behavior of grounding is a disaster. There is no way she can feel better in this deteriorating situation. Before the onset of her condition she used to feel depressed and angry; now she suffers unrelenting pain as well.

Her physiology is not very much involved, but the doctor she goes to has warned her to expect the bloating and diarrhea that is often part of the problem. Ellen wishes he hadn't mentioned it. Now that she knows about it, she worries that it's going to happen. If you'll remember, Drs. Bohr and Barsky warned against talking to patients about the possibility of additional symptoms because they often develop them. Suggestion is often a powerful motivator.

Even though everyone she asks supports her and tells her she has to do what she is doing, Ellen is aware that when she grounds Samantha, she feels her relationship with her slip further away. Even if she didn't have fibromyalgia, there is no way she could feel good as long as she's trapped between what she knows is right—the grounding—and the unraveling relationship with a child she depends upon for love. She realizes she shouldn't depend so much on Samantha for love but who else does she have?

Ellen is involved in the most destructive situation that a human being can find oneself in. She is in conflict. Part of her wants to hold tight to what she is choosing to do: keep Samantha grounded no matter how the girl treats her.

Another part of her wants to give up, let Samantha do whatever she wants. This part is thinking, "I'm going to die unless I figure a way out of this situation. Why can't someone help me?" But no one helps her. She has had a few hysterical talks with her ex, but he is adamant. He keeps reminding her that he has new obligations and there is nothing he can do.

In her conflict with Samantha, Ellen's actions and thoughts are similar to the actions and thoughts I had that kept me trying to drive my car a hundred miles an hour on the autobahn. When I slowed down the car stopped shaking. Even though Ellen's doing the "right thing," she is pushing her life past what her love and belonging genes are willing to accept. These genes know nothing about her divorce or her problems with Samantha. All her genes know is that she is not getting them what they want—more love. The unwanted parts of her unhappy total behavior are attacking her with pain and fatigue.

What Help is Available for Ellen?

If her doctor gives her a little time and she is able to tell him what she is struggling with at home, he may make some connection between her fibromyalgia and her problems with Samantha. But while he may sense she needs some care and attention and would like to give her more time, there is often no provision in present-day medical practice to provide this time. For many people with fairly good relationships and less behavioral symptoms, an attentive, sympathetic doctor may go a long way to help. But with Ellen's symptoms, she needs more than attention. She needs to find out what to do specifically with Samantha that will get more love back into that relationship.

Starting in Chapter Six and continuing in Chapters Seven and Eight, I will explain in detail how Ellen, Karen and someone you haven't met yet named Sue, can learn new, more need-satisfying total behaviors to deal with the important people in their lives.

Lacking that knowledge, it is obvious that choosing a doctor who cares for you and listens to you is more important with a condition like fibromyalgia than it is with a more physically destructive but in a sense more treatable disease, such as rheumatoid arthritis.

In fact, in the last sentence in the second paragraph of his article, Dr. Groopman states: "The debate over diagnosis and treatment has become so heated that it has polarized medical specialists; choosing a doctor has become tantamount to adopting an ideological position."

That polarization has divided practitioners into two almost equal halves. One half sees the need for more time with patients; the other half believes that the more attention they pay, the more their symptoms will increase. But whichever half the doctor is in, few doctors want to tell the sufferers to get counseling.

Dr. Groopman points out in the article that patients with this condition react badly to the suggestion that their problem is psychological and take that suggestion as a rejection by their doctor. Karen saw two psychiatrists and neither asked her in any detail about her marriage. Without hardly getting to know her, they both offered drugs.

What Ellen and those like her are offered by doctors is summarized in Dr. Groopman's article as: "judicious doses of psychotropic medicines and analgesics, a graduated exercise program, and—perhaps most significant—the promise that the patient's suffering would be taken seriously."

If a doctor were treating Ellen with the above widely accepted, but totally nonspecific regimen, it is clear from the article that she would get little relief. If this treatment were beneficial, there would not have been 750 women jammed into that ballroom at the Westin. The only thing in that regimen that I as a psychiatrist take exception to, is the use of psychotropic drugs in the absence of any specific, diagnosable psychiatric disease.

The use of these drugs for fibromyalgia is no more supported by research than the use of antibiotics is supported for a viral infection. Psychotropic drugs are strong and change the physiology of the brain in many ways that are not yet understood and may add to the problem. My contention that psychiatric medication is given to fibromyalgics without research support, is confirmed by Dr. Groopman. He tells of a close friend of some thirty years whom he calls Liz Albright. She teaches at an elite New England college and received a diagnosis of fibromyalgia with associated chronic-fatigue and irritable bowel syndromes in 1994.

Liz, who goes to a local internist in the Boston area recently told Dr. Groopman, "You need to believe I'm really sick, not just complaining." She explained that for her fatigue, she was given Ritalin, and for her insomnia, Ambien. She told him, "I am probably addicted but the doctor keeps giving them because he has no answers." Recently she has been given Prozac but it hasn't made much difference.

The problem is that without pathology, many doctors, including psychiatrists, feel helpless. It is my hope that the ideas in this book will not only help patients, but also doctors, to see that the pain and disability may be unwanted components of chosen total behaviors that are disconnecting sufferers from the people and the love they need.

My message to Ellen and all women like her is you don't have an imaginary problem. You have a real problem with a real person in your life and, in most instances, there is nothing extraordinary about the total behavior you are choosing to deal with that person. You believe that what you are choosing to do is the right thing to do. Is it any wonder that the feeling and physiological components of a "correct" total behavior, such as grounding your daughter, is tearing you apart both physically and mentally? You'd have to be completely insensitive to ignore what Samantha's doing and go cheerfully about your life.

Do any of you reading this book honestly think that whatever fibromyalgia is, it has nothing to do with the relationship problems I have been explaining? And of the six million, mostly educated, middle-class, Caucasian women like you who have been diagnosed with this condition, isn't it very likely that a problem with a child is as frustrating as a sexual problem in or out of marriage?

Several million educated women like Liz Albright, who have high expectations of love, recognition, career, marriage, child rearing, and themselves, are not coming close to realizing these expectations. I am asking them to accept that their frustrations, and especially, the total behaviors they are using to deal with them, may have a lot to do with their condition. But I am not asking them to accept that there is nothing they can do for themselves. I believe exactly the opposite.

There is no substitute for the love and belonging our genes demand. No doctor can prescribe a medication or a treatment to replace it. But based on Choice Theory, there is much you can do to help yourself both give and get more of the love you need to be happy.

Creativity: Another Important Component of Choice Theory

While you wait for an effective medical treatment that doesn't take into account the relationship problems I have been explaining, I ask you to weigh the further possibility that the pain and disability you are experiencing may be caused by something few people—doctors and patients alike—ever consider. This element, *creativity*, is very much a part of every total behavior you choose. It can affect any or all of its components. Could it be that the more creative you are, the more you are susceptible to "diseases" such as fibromyalgia?

Creativity rarely plays a dominant role in most of the routine behaviors you choose daily. You are rarely aware of it except in situations like an unwanted thought running through your mind or an unwanted behavior such as avoiding cracks. These are good examples of how creative your mind can be even though they are not even close to the disabling pain and fatigue of fibromyalgia.

What I believe and will now try to explain is that our inherent creativity plays such an important role in our lives that it can create something as overwhelming and mysterious as fibromyalgia. When we are creative, there is no limit to how far our creativity can take us. Our dreams are the best example. Whatever we know about them, one thing is certain: there are no bounds to what we can do in our dreams. Dreams can even bring life to what is inanimate; I recently dreamed my computer was alive.

Anything you see around you in the world, which is not natural, has been created by someone—art, music, even athleticism never seen before. For example, the way

Michael Jordan played basketball was so creative that at times, even he was surprised. Basically, I believe that anything you have perceived, thought about, acted on, felt, or any physiology you have experienced, your brain can create on its own. I feel sure my brain created the tachycardia episodes I suffered for several years with no cause ever being found.

If you can hear a voice, your brain can create voices, as in auditory hallucinations. I don't believe you could hallucinate a voice if you'd never heard one. Beethoven was deaf, but still created beautiful music. But if he'd never have heard music, I don't think he could have created it. If you have ever suffered any pain, weakness, fatigue, insomnia, stomach upset, or bladder irritation, I think your brain could recreate, expand on, or embellish this experience and offer it to you as a symptom.

But I am not claiming that all symptoms are created. If your complaint is caused by a disease or an accident, you suffer from pathology and usually need a doctor's intervention. For example, if you are infected with a strep throat or hit on the head with a hammer, you need help. There is no behavior you can choose on your own that will get rid of the strep or heal the blow of the hammer.

Alternately, if fibromyalgia is caused by your trying to solve a relationship problem by attempting to control someone else's behavior by choosing an ineffective total behavior like grounding, then you can choose to change that behavior for a better one. Until you can figure out how to do this though, you may suffer terribly because there is no limit to how much pain your brain can create. The created pain can be much more severe than if it were caused by some specific pathology because the extent of the pathology, in most instances, will limit the pain. A small intrusion by a vertebral disc into your spinal cord would hurt less than a large intrusion.

You might also wonder, as a creative total behavior, is fibromyalgia an anomaly, a rare occurrence that only the six million women so identified suffer? Hardly. Dr. Peter Breggin[3] states that Schizophrenia, usually labeled a mental illness, is in many instances a creative total thinking behavior. It is no more a disease with a known and verified pathology than is fibromyalgia. But like the internists who can't accept that fibromyalgia is not a disease, the majority of the psychiatrists in the world, when dealing with schizophrenia, ask and answer affirmatively a variation of Dr. Groopman's question, "How could so many people be so crazy and not be suffering from a disease?"

Attention Deficit Disorder (ADD) is another very recently created "disease." Clinical depression is another. The list goes on and on. The mental illness bible, the *DSM-IV*, in which hundreds of mental illnesses are catalogued, are all accurate descriptions of creative total behaviors with no definitive brain pathology to support them. What we are seeing is that there are a lot of unhappy, lonely people who deal creatively with their unhappiness in a wide variety of ways. What this shows is there is almost no limit to human creativity.

If you want to know what a mental illness really is, Alzheimer's disease fits that label to a tee. The Alzheimer brain has been destroyed by an unknown process; but believe me, it is a real disease.

The Creative Process in More Detail

Every day a few people in the world figure out something so new and so superior to anything like it, that the whole world applauds. Then a year later someone trumps that card and comes up with something even better. On a smaller scale, most of us are constantly getting creative ideas that make improvements in our lives. Sometimes when we are stuck, we come up with such a creative answer we can't get over it and want to shout it to the rooftops. It is this creativity that separates us from machines. Computers can do many mental tasks faster and better than we can, but so far, they cannot create. Only living organisms can create.

What I claim is our creativity is always operating. When we are stuck for something to do—we call it "putting on our thinking caps"—sometimes our creativity kicks in and sometimes it doesn't. Our creativity is there, we use it all the time, but we can't count on it or come close to controlling it. It may or may not give us an answer but it's always doing the best it can. One thing it doesn't do (and this can be both a blessing and a curse) is give up.

I'm sure you've all had the experience of being insulted by someone and thought to yourself, I'd have given anything for a snappy comeback. But nothing came. The incident was brief and you thought you'd forgotten about it. But your creativity didn't forget. Suddenly, totally out of context, the retort you wished for at the time popped into your mind. As late as it was, you still got a good feeling when it happened. This is positive creativity.

Unfortunately, creativity can be harmful as well as helpful. If you have any long-term, unsolved relationship problems, your creativity usually gets involved and stays involved. And what it does can often be quite destructive. Certainly, if it produces fibromyalgia, I'm sure you wish it had never poked its nose into your business.

Humans probably became as creative as they are because people who were not creative could not survive in competition with those who were more creative. This is simple evolutionary truth. Whether we like it or not, our creativity is here to stay. I also believe that our creativity continually monitors our unhappiness. It keeps in touch with how effectively we are satisfying our genetic needs.

That doesn't mean it isn't available to help us when we are happy; it's always available and research has shown that happy people are almost never creative in self-destructive ways. For example, the longest-lived, healthiest, and happiest of all occupational groups are symphony orchestra conductors, certainly a very creative and fulfilling line of work.

In this book, however, I'm not focusing on the creativity of happy people. I'm concerned about your unhappiness, the creativity it engenders, and how it may become more and more involved with your feelings and your physiology. Let's go back to Ellen, the single mother struggling with her fifteen-year-old daughter. She is desperate for a solution to this very real relationship problem.

Long before she was afflicted with fibromyalgia, Ellen was confronted with the loneliness of her life, and her self-destructive creativity got involved. She must have been unhappy about the fact that her husband left her for a younger woman. She had to take over the complete care of a puzzled eight-year-old who missed her father terribly. Some of Samantha's search for love at parties may be tied to that loss.

There is also the possibility that Ellen is frustrated at work and to add to that she may be burdened with a mother who criticizes her for losing her husband. I'm not claiming that all single mothers are seriously unhappy, but Ellen is marked as extremely unhappy by her pain and disability. If she knew anything about her needs, she could figure out it is her need to love and be loved that is frustrated and the frustration is increasing.

At the point I introduced her in this chapter, she was at her wit's end with her daughter. She literally didn't know what to do. The grounding wasn't working and she had no one to help her. She was miserable. Her creativity, continually monitoring her unhappiness, kept prodding her with pain to remind her to get more love in her life. What it might have created besides the pain was a new thought. For example, it might tempt her with what would be an unacceptable solution before she became fibro-myalgic such as: "Go to your father. I'm out of here."

When you are desperate from pain and lack of love, don't depend on your ability to turn down what your creativity offers you. At best, if you understand what it's trying to do, you may resist some of its more bizarre suggestions. The more severe your relationship problem, the less you may be able to turn down its offerings. It was her creative system that led a woman in South Carolina a few years ago to think: *I'll drown my two boys so I can go to my lover unencumbered. He's told me he won't have me with my children.*

This lonely woman is now serving life for the murder of her children. I'm not trying to excuse her for what she did. We don't have to accept any creative suggestion that enters our mind but when we are desperate to hold on to a relationship, there is no predicting what our creativity will suggest or what we'll do.

I also want to emphasize that our creativity is neither bad nor good. It has no morality. It just creates. What it creates can be very good, of no value, or be very harmful to us or to other people. It can get involved in how we feel by causing us pain in any part of our body that can feel pain, although in the beginning it tends to stick to areas where we may have had pain before such as headache and backache.

A possible purpose of this creative pain is to augment the usual pain of your frustration and tell you your life is not working for you the way you want. The only way you can tell this pain from the pain of a real disease is to look for the pathology. If there is no pathology, then you should always suspect that your creativity is hard at work.

But there can also be a lot of pathology, as in rheumatoid arthritis, and still much of the pain may be caused by creative ways to handle unsatisfying relationships. Either way, whether it is created pain, pathological pain, or a combination of both, you will still be better off if you can solve any relationship problems you may have.

Now I'd like to explain an indirect function of your creativity. It may create so much pain and disability that you will literally forget about your relationship problem and concentrate all your effort on your symptoms. I have the feeling that this may be happening with some of the women who attended that meeting in the Westin Hotel. Ellen, too, may get so deeply involved in her fibromyalgia that she begins to lose interest in her daughter's behavior, kind of *que sera, sera*.

This is what may have happened with Liz Albright, the college teacher mentioned in Dr. Groopman's article, who actually quit her job at an elite New England college. This is very unusual behavior for a fifty-one-year-old, educated, professional woman with such a good job. It may have occurred at the suggestion of her creativity, which may have urged her to just drop it all and concentrate on her illness. As Dr. Groopman tells her story he explains:

> Finally, last year she gave in and took time off from teaching because of the pain, fatigue, and episodes of what is commonly referred to as "fibrofog," or the inability to think clearly.
>
> We talked about the nomenclature, and about how fibromyalgia seems to be merging with chronic-fatigue syndrome. She said, "Chronic fatigue has become a humiliating term—the Yuppie disease, begging to be laughed at... Fibromyalgia is more socially acceptable." When I mentioned that doctors call fibromyalgia a wastebasket diagnosis, she bristled: "They'd love to throw me away."

Following the thesis of this book, my guess is that Liz's conflict may be with both power and belonging, and she was looking for a way to escape from what may have been a frustrating situation for a woman at an elite, often male-dominated educational institution. She may be complaining about more important people in her life than the doctors when she finally exclaimed to Dr. Groopman, *'They'd love to throw me away.'*

If Ellen gives up her job and stays home instead of running away from home and leaving her daughter to her father, she may disappear almost completely into her fibromyalgia. She'd tell her daughter to fend for herself, that she's too sick to take care of her, which she would be if she got some additional creative symptoms or her creativity increased her pain.

Samantha, who does love her mother and does know that Ellen is trying to protect her with the grounding—all teens know that much—may be alarmed enough by her mother's sickness to respond positively and stay home nights and weekends and to nurse her mother. Maybe

Samantha thought Ellen was treating her too much like a baby and now this "disease" has helped Samantha to feel grown up in a more constructive way than partying.

Now it's time to turn to another Choice Theory concept, our *quality world*. This concept may explain why this is more a disease of white, middle-class women and seen more in the United States than in other countries.

5

Who Will Never Suffer from Fibromyalgia?

This is the fourth time I've attempted this chapter. I got the idea for this rewrite from my creativity at about 4:00 a.m. this morning, a time it's often very active. I guess it had taken on the assignment of working on this chapter after I spent eight hours on it yesterday and gave up dissatisfied. What frustrated me and, I believe, triggered my creativity, was one of the most intriguing puzzles of fibromyalgia: Why does this "disease" primarily afflict economically comfortable, young to middle-aged Caucasian women?

Now I am energized by the idea that popped into my head early this morning: *fibromyalgia is not a disease of street people*, those who wander around our cities self-disenfranchised. They may be alcoholic, drug addicted, tubercular, and homeless. They may suffer from malnutrition or injuries, die from exposure to the cold, but I can't picture any of them suffering from severe pain of an unknown origin.

As soon as this idea came to me, I immediately compared the people I've seen wandering the streets for years with the 750 suffering women packed into the ballroom of the posh Westin, all desperately hoping to get relief from their pain. To put it bluntly, there were no street people in that group.

In fact, if there is a complete opposite to whatever it is like to be living on the streets, it would be the women in that group. Except for a few bag ladies, the street people are almost all men. Fibromyalgics are ninety percent women. The people who choose to live on the streets have little concern for their health or comfort. In contrast, these women are totally concerned with their health and comfort and had been reasonably concerned with it well before they became ill. Street people have abandoned their families. The women at the Westin, even with their pain, are trying very hard to play an important role in their families.

Most importantly, the street people have few aspirations except to be left alone. I believe that before these women at the Westin became "sick" they had high aspirations for themselves, both as homemakers and in their careers, and had equally high or even higher aspirations for their children. They also expected a lot both socially and sexually from their marriages. But they did more than expect a lot from life. Before they became ill, many like Liz Albright were capable, successful women. They took the idea that women have an important place in the world seriously and saw themselves more as givers than as takers from the milieu they lived in.

Above all, these were not women who ever expected that anyone would even intimate that they were mentally ill. They were justifiably angry when some of their physicians suggested that their pain might be in their head. As explained in the last chapter, there was nothing imaginary about their pain. When they became ill they became depressed, but it was not because they had failed at anything or lost their family or friends. It was because the pain made it impossible for them to function at the level they aspired to. They were depressed just as a competitive runner would become depressed if he/she blew out a knee and could no longer compete.

Unlike the street folks who seem to accept that they are not connected to the important people in their lives, as I read about these women in books on fibromyalgia what struck me was how connected many of them seemed to be to their mates and families. Over and over I looked to their marriages and like Karen, many of them had what they claimed to be a good marriage where their husband was a major source of support for their suffering. I asked myself, am I wrong in my belief that they are not satisfied with their relationships?

But then as I got the idea of comparing them with the disenfranchised who frequent soup kitchens, it struck me that what had gone wrong in the lives of the women with fibromyalgia was not because they were inadequate. It was quite the opposite. They, themselves, were willing to work hard to try to satisfy their aspirations. What they did was aspire to more for themselves than they were able to fulfill and expect more of others than they were able to get.

As Mr. Micawber says in *David Copperfield*, "Annual income twenty pounds, annual expenditure nineteen six, result happiness. Annual income twenty pounds, annual expenditure twenty pounds ought six, result misery." No matter how much you may accomplish, happiness is being able to aspire within a range you can achieve. Get beyond that range, especially with the important people in your life, and you will not be happy. I drove my car on the autobahn beyond that range.

Choice Theory explains that inside our brain we have a place where we store our level of aspiration. I call that place our *quality world*. It is a small, simulated series of pictures in our memory in which we store the experiences in our lives that have felt very good. For us, these are the quality experiences.

Starting with our mother, many of our good experiences with her feel so good we put a picture of her into our quality world and keep it there for the rest of our lives. We also put pictures of all the important people in our lives into this world. These are the people we turn to whenever we are lonely or frustrated. We depend on them to help us through our frustration. But as much as we may do for them, if we expect too much from them, we are going to be disappointed.

We also put pictures of things into our quality worlds such as a nice home or a fancy car. We even put things we don't want to own in our quality world like a beautiful day for the picnic we have been planning for a month. If we are unable to get the things we want, we will be frustrated. Beyond a stolen shopping cart and the few possessions it can hold, the street people aspire to very little. In their own way, they may be happier than many of us who have so much more.

Most of us also put ideas or systems of belief into our quality world. The more we believe, as in religion or politics, the more we want others to believe the same way. Choice Theory is an important belief in my quality world. When people write me and tell me how much this belief has improved their lives, I feel very good. But try as we may, if no one agrees with what we believe, we will be very frustrated. To avoid that frustration the street folks don't usually try to spread their beliefs. The more we try, the more chance there is for serious frustration.

But one thing in their quality world that we share with many street people is the idea that we should find ways to feel good, whether those ways are need-satisfying or not. For many street people and for huge numbers of those who are not, the picture of using an addictive substance like alcohol is very much a part of their quality world. Addicting substances provide direct, immediate pleasure without our needing anyone or anything else to feel good.

The late Alexander Wolcott put it better than anyone else I've ever heard of when he said, "Everything I like is either illegal, immoral or fattening." This is a perfect explanation for the fact that there is no morality in our quality world. Feeling good is the only requirement for admission. No one is exempt from wanting to feel good without expending much effort. Therefore, none of us is exempt from moral failings, yet I still believe we are all responsible for what we do. The fact that it feels good is hardly an excuse for harming ourselves or others.

The final aspect of our quality world that few of us think about is the role we, ourselves, play in that world. The more we picture ourselves behaving in ways that expect a lot from ourselves, the more difficult it is to satisfy these pictures, especially if others in our life do not cooperate.

Most street people don't ask much of themselves. The pictures of themselves in their quality world are very simple. All they expect is to find an entryway to sleep in at night, food from a dumpster or a mission, and/or the skill to panhandle enough money to get a jug of wine. I am not advocating this kind of life. What I am trying to explain is why their lives are not filled with frustration.

What I described in the last chapter is that when we are frustrated our creativity can come up with pain and disability. But I believe that the frustration most associated with fibromyalgia is as much associated with what we expect of ourselves as what we expect of others. I think that fibromyalgia is a "disease" of capable women. These women expect that when a problem comes up in their lives they can solve it or, if they are sick, they can go to a good doctor and it will be solved.

Unfortunately, fibromyalgia is as frustrating to their doctor as it is to them and this doubles their frustration. That they see themselves so capable because they are capable, makes it so hard for them to accept that their pain is indirectly of their own doing. The test of my theory will be for you to put it to work in your life. I believe that if you are able to reduce your expectations of both yourself and others in your quality world, you will be better able to satisfy your needs. This will provide you with relief from your pain.

Let me make explicit about what I am suggesting. I believe there are a very important group of pictures that are much more often found in the quality worlds of middle- to upper-middle-class fibromyalgic women than women in general. You picture yourself being able to do many things and do them all well, in some cases more than most other women in our society might even attempt.

I believe that you may have to modify these pictures if you are to get back your health.

Are you a woman who holds a responsible, demanding job, who seldom says no to your boss? Are you a woman who on the surface accepts less pay for your work than a man but seethes inside at this injustice? Do you picture yourself as a woman who takes care of a perfect home by herself without help? A woman who never shirks from giving her kids every opportunity and who drives them all over town? If you make a mistake, do you call yourself stupid? Do you cater to your husband? Do you diet and exercise to stay attractive? And when you occasionally wonder if you're appreciated, do you try to banish that thought from your mind?

This *superwoman* or *supermom* is alive and well *in the quality worlds* of many middle- to upper-middle-class, Caucasian women all over the country. I believe a significant number of these supermoms and ex-supermoms, alive but hardly well, were sitting in the Westin ballroom that day in the spring of 2000. I also believe that there are a 100 of you for every superdad and I doubt if, on close inspection, there are no more than a few superdads who would rate as high on the super scale as you do. I believe that this is the reason for the 10:1 ratio of women with fibromyalgia over men. It is the superwoman whose creative system steps in to stop her when she drives her life so close to the red line.

To slow these women down, it takes something like fibromyalgia. And with these women it takes a lot of fibromyalgia. These are the women who have the most serious cases, the most creative symptoms and the ones who demand the most from their doctors. I can only point out that if you have this *I-can-do-it-all* picture in your quality world, only you can do something about it.

Remember, it's your quality world. You control what goes in and what comes out. It can be a world filled with wonderful people and depicting an exciting, creative life as long as you don't want too much from it. My suggestion to you is to use one of the most famous sentences in American literature and say to the superwoman in your quality world, "It's enough, already! Keep quiet and don't protest because if you do, 'Frankly my dear, I don't give a damn!' " [4]

6

Replace the Seven Deadly Habits

This is the chapter I've been promising since Chapter One: what you can do to keep your relationships strong and satisfying. Before I started to write it, I did some thinking and decided that this was the time to ask Karen for the help she'd offered when we met in Chapter Two. I called, told her I'd finished the first five chapters, asked if she would read them, and then come to see me to give me her feedback before I started on Chapter Six. This way I'd have an idea whether I was on the right track.

She only had the chapters for a week when she called and said she'd like very much to talk with me about them and was quite interested in what I was going to suggest in Chapter Six. I didn't ask her if she liked what she read; if she didn't like it she wouldn't have offered to come in.

I was surprised when I opened the door. She wasn't alone. A man was with her whom she introduced as her husband, Gary. He was about her age, nice looking with thinning sandy hair, a well-trimmed beard, slender, about five-ten, with a springy step like an athlete. They seemed to be very comfortable together, no tension that I could see, and I got the impression he wanted to be there with her.

He started to talk even before we sat down. "I guess you're surprised to see me. I hope it's okay, but Karen got so involved in what you sent her, I asked if I could read it. I'm a dentist, I can relate to what you wrote, that stuff about pain and total behavior. I struggle with patients who complain a lot about jaw pain. It's even been given a name, *temporal mandibular syndrome*. That syndrome puzzles a lot of us. It's similar to what Karen has in that it doesn't have any pathology to support it. You must have heard about it."

I nodded, saying, "I've heard of it and you're right. That pain could be another example of creativity. I don't think there's any limit to what we can create when our creativity gets involved. Do you have any questions about anything you read?"

Karen said, "We've done more than read it; we've talked a lot about it. What you wrote in Chapter Two about when we were so happy and how it seems to have slipped away. We've been closer since we read that."

"It's true, we have," Gary said, "What we haven't been able to figure out is why we lost our happiness. It's not just the sickness. We were unhappy for a long time before she got sick. That's why I wanted to come in. Where did we go wrong? It's mysterious. It's like she said, our love just seemed to slip away."

"Didn't you both accept that what happened to your marriage was normal? That almost all your friends have gone through the same thing or worse?"

Karen added, "That's it. It is normal, so normal that I guess we did accept it. You seem to know the story, so many of our friends, or I guess they used to be our friends, are divorced. Once a couple gets divorced, nothing is the same. It's hard to stay friends, they're uncomfortable and we're uncomfortable. Divorce screws everything up."

I said, "I'm pretty sure there's a reason for what happened. I'd like to explain it and see what you think. But first, I wonder if you have anything to ask me about the other stuff I wrote. You know, the needs, total behavior and what I referred to as your quality world in the last chapter."

For a moment, they just looked at each other, then Gary said, "The needs made sense. I never thought about them as being in our genes, but something drove me to become a dentist and to do all I've done. It could be power. But we love each other and I did a lot of this for her. The power need is satisfied but what's happened to our love?"

"The quality world makes sense, too," Karen commented. "He's still in mine, but not as strong as he used to be. I don't understand."

Gary was quick to add, "The love's still there somewhere, I mean, I feel it."

"He's right. We haven't lost it. We've been talking, I mean really talking more in the last week than we've talked in the last year. I was happy he showed that much interest. I didn't ask him to come in today, he wanted to."

Then Gary said, "It's what you wrote in Chapter Four. I think you've got a point, but Karen's having a lot of trouble with it. It's what you said about choosing everything we do. She just can't buy your concept that somehow—and I know you call it an indirect choice—she's choosing all this pain."

"In Chapter Four, I didn't say you were choosing the pain. I said—"

Karen interrupted, "I know what you said, that the pain is a part of my behavior—"

I corrected her, "Not just behavior, a part of your total behavior."

"Okay, total behavior. But the thing is I wasn't that unhappy, I really wasn't. It's just too much pain to be explained that way. It's out of proportion."

Gary added, "That part bothered me, too. But then I thought about this patient with all the jaw pain. There's nothing wrong with his jaw. That's also out of proportion, too."

"How about when you were happy?" I addressed both of them, "Are you willing to say you were choosing to be happy?"

They both looked at each other. Karen then took his hand, held it up to her cheek and said, "I can't remember anything about choosing it. But, I'll tell you, we were very happy."

"I guess you misunderstood. I wasn't talking about the fact you were happy. I'm asking you if you can recollect that you were choosing your happiness. It's the choosing the total behavior that's the new idea. Didn't you choose to treat each other in ways that had a lot to do with how you felt? Were you aware you were choosing all the things that went along with your happiness? If your parents asked if you were happy, what would you have told them?"

"Her parents never asked but mine asked all the time. They were thrilled we were so happy. I guess you could say it was the way we chose to act and think. That's what made us happy."

"He's right, I can remember figuring out how we could both get home during the day for half an hour to make love. It's just the idea of choosing, it's such a new idea. I'm having trouble getting used to it."

"I knew you'd have this trouble, everyone does. That's why I wanted you to come in today. I'm glad you came. I'm glad you both came. But when you became unhappy, didn't you choose all the sniping, criticizing and not listening to each other that Karen talked about when she came in by herself? Wasn't that chosen? Aren't those choices the acting and thinking parts of unhappiness?"

Karen said, "It's easier when I hear you explain it. We don't choose the feelings, we choose the other parts."

"You don't choose the physiology either—the bloating and the bladder irritation—some of the body things Dr. Groopman talked about. No one chooses those."

Gary then asked, "But what I still don't understand is why our marriage seemed almost doomed to go downhill? We have a lot better marriage than our parents have but that's not much consolation."

I said, "It's not just marriage that concerns me. It's the whole world. Look at the front page of the paper. Watch the evening news."

Karen said, "That's another thing we argue about. I don't want to hear about all that misery. I think he watches it because it makes him feel better. You know, like he's so much better off. But I hate it, it doesn't make me feel better. I feel worse."

"I guess it does make me feel better. Like, when a friend's marriage breaks up I feel glad it's not mine. But what does this have to do with us?"

"It may have more to do with you than you think. Do you see any group of people in the world who are living together, like in the Middle East or in Northern Ireland, who are getting along better now than they used to?"

Karen said, "But that's politics, it doesn't have anything to do with us."

"She's right. Why bring that up?"

"Okay, I'm sorry, I don't want to confuse you. I'm just trying to point out that human beings have a hard time getting along with each other over the long haul no matter where they are or what situation they're in, especially when they're forced to be together for a long time, like in marriage. But how about parents and kids? Are you on better terms with your kids now that they're teenagers than when they were little? I think Karen told me on the phone you have a couple of teenagers."

"Teenagers are tough. There's been a lot less joy around our house since they became teenagers. They're sullen. Why are they always so sullen?" Gary asked.

"I think that in some ways your kids kind of mirror you. Were they happier when they were younger?"

"Karen said, "They were, but why? We love them and they have all the things they want."

"Could it be the school? Were they happier in elementary school?"

Gary said, "They loved elementary school, but it stopped when they hit middle school."

Karen interjected, "But they really like the high school. It's where their friends are and they like the extracurricular activities, especially the sports."

"How about the classes?"

"Most of the are okay and they like the teachers."

But Gary added, "They hate the homework and all the pressure. They really lay it on the kids in that private school. I never came close to spending as much time as they do every night on homework. And then it never really seems to get done."

"He's right there. Every evening we keep after them to finish their assignments."

"It's a nightmare and I think it's even affecting our marriage."

I said, "How about work? Do you know many people who are happy at work, especially if they have to do a lot of things they don't like doing?"

Gary said, "Work seems fine for many of my dentist and doctor friends as long as they can make it in private practice like I can. But the ones who work for HMOs hate it because they can't practice the way they want to. I give that guy with the jaw pain a little TLC whenever he comes in and my office manager talks to him a while on the phone when he calls. It helps."

"All I'm trying to point out is that when we're in any locked-in relationship—political, marriage, family, school or work—it's hard to stay happy. Would you like to hear my theory on why this is?"

Karen said, "Not if it's just a theory. It seems to me you promised more."

"Well, it is a theory. I call it Choice Theory. Remember, I mentioned it starting in the first chapter. But it's a theory you can use. You may not realize it, but you and Gary have been using it this past week and you said it's been the best week in a long time. If you can accept the theory and use it, there's a good chance you can turn your marriage around."

Gary said, "It sounds like we'd both have to use it. Suppose I want to use it and she doesn't?"

"No problem, that happens all the time. It can still work. It may just take a little longer. But you're here together. I'm assuming you're both here to learn something. You've been using it for a week. Why not keep using it?"

Karen said, "Do you use it? I don't like being a guinea pig."

"My wife and I use it all the time. It's become so much a part of our lives, it's almost like breathing. It's called Choice Theory because you choose it, or at least the acting and thinking parts, like I explained in Chapter Four. It seems to me that in your marriage it's working already. You don't seem at all like the couple Karen described when she came in last time."

Gary said, "It's because we're treating each other better."

I said, "Do you know why?"

Gary explained, "Because of what you wrote, that part about happiness and unhappiness. We'd be fools to keep treating each other the same way we were."

They both looked at me as if for approval.

"You've been making better choices for a week. Now you need to learn how to make better choices for the rest of your lives. Better choices, that's what Choice Theory's all about."

Now they were interested and looked at me for more. I started in the same way I almost always start when I explain Choice Theory to someone new. "See my phone? What if it rang right now and I picked it up and talked for a moment and hung up. Then I asked you, why did I just pick up the phone?"

They chimed in together, "Because it rang."

"That's what everybody says. Look, I'm not trying to be smart but I don't think anyone's ever picked up a phone because it rang. Only answering machines do that."

They seemed curious and I went on, "I claim that I chose to pick up that phone just like I choose everything I do. You both know that lots of times the phone rings and you choose to let it ring. I'll bet you didn't answer the phone years ago when you sneaked home to make love. That ring really doesn't make you do anything. I'm just using the phone example to explain another theory, actually the opposite of Choice Theory. I call it *external control theory*. I've got some explaining to do, but your use of that theory is what changed your marriage from happy to unhappy. External control is responsible for destroying the marriages of almost all your divorced friends. You didn't use it for a week and already you're happier."

Karen said, "Are you saying my sister's divorced because she answers her phone when it rings? C'mon."

"I've got to explain some more but I guess you could say that the answer to your questions is yes."

Gary said, "If we don't answer the phone because it rings, what's the ring for?"

Karen said, "Yeah, if it hadn't rung, you wouldn't have answered it. What's the big deal about answering a phone?"

"Okay. All I'm trying to explain is the ring doesn't make you do anything. What it does is give you information that someone out there wants to talk to someone here. I use the ring to point out that all we can give each other is information. Like I'm doing now. But there's a huge difference between giving each other information—that's Choice Theory—and trying to make the other act on it—that's external control. This is a difference most people don't understand. You don't ever have to answer the phone if you don't want to. And you don't have to act on any information anyone or any machine gives you unless you want to. On your way home from here, you can run every red light if you want to and keep running them until you get into an accident."

Karen began to catch on, "You're saying we answer the phone because we want to, not because it rings. Right?"

"Exactly. People tell you to do things all day long but it's up to you whether you do them. External control is the psychology the whole world uses. Wherever you see misery it's almost always because people are trying to control each other."

Gary added, "Karen, remember how your sister's husband was on her case about her weight as soon as they had their first baby. Jim never let up."

I said, "A perfect example of external control. His nagging, and I'm sure what she did when he nagged, killed that marriage. It doesn't matter if they got divorced. Nagging killed their love."

Karen added, "You may be right. You know what she did about his nagging?" I shook my head. "Whenever they'd go out, she'd order the richest dessert. Those 'Death by Chocolate' creations drove him nuts. They'd be out with customers because he had to do a lot of entertaining and he'd have to keep his mouth shut. She'd just sit there slowly eating those desserts and smiling.

It happened over and over when we were with them. I thought he was going to have a coronary."

Gary said, "You say that theory you call external control is the world's psychology and that we all use it?"

"Not everybody, but unhappy people do. The unhappier you are, the more you use it or resist it as Karen's sister did. It plays hell with marriage. Even if it doesn't kill a marriage, it sucks all the joy out of it."

Karen asked, "So, tell us more about this psychology that few people have ever heard of."

"Some people are hearing about external control but not so many that it makes much difference in most people's lives. But right now I'm not worried about how many people know about it, I'm concerned about you and your bad experience with it. What I'm trying to do is teach you about it and then teach both of you how to replace external control with Choice Theory. External control is the old psychology that disconnects people and drives them apart. Choice Theory is the new psychology that connects people and keeps them close."

Gary added, "But you keep calling it a psychology. You're a psychiatrist, you think in those terms. The people I know don't think psychology, they just do things."

"It may seem that way to you but it's really not. People think a lot about what to do and how to do it when they're having difficulty getting along with each other. You and Gary may not call it psychology, but if you come up with ways to get along like you used to, then you'll be aware you're using psychology. Gary, you think a lot about that patient you have with jaw pain and you've decided to give him some attention. Karen, you think about how you're going to get your kids to do their homework five nights a week. Gary, you think about how, with all her pain, you're going to persuade Karen to make love with you. I said make love like you used to, not just have sex. Basically, everyone in the world uses psychology when they want to persuade anyone to do something they might not want to do. The only time you don't think in terms of psychology, or whatever you want to call it, is when you're getting along great with everyone in your life. External control psychology is a plague on all our lives."

Gary said, "Wow, you seem pretty worked up about that. But you say you can't control people. I say you can. I run a busy office with two other dentists, four dental hygienists, and three general office staff, and I control them all. I think I'm a nice guy but I call the shots."

"I guess I didn't make myself clear. I should have said you can only control people physically. You can't control what they think or what they want. As I explained in the last chapter, you can't control what's in their quality worlds. If external control couldn't control people physically, no one would use it. It works for you because the people you employ are afraid of you. But what happens to your relationship with them if you threaten them? And will they still treat your patients the way you want them to? Show me someone really happy and I'll show you a person who isn't trying to control anyone and no one's trying to control him. That's why we get along so much better with our friends than with our family."

Karen said, "What do you mean?"

"If you want to get along with your friends, you don't try to control them. That's the difference between a good friend and a spouse. You can take a break from a friend if you have a disagreement. You can't really take a break from Gary. You've stayed together but you haven't been as happy as you'd like to be for a long time."

"But what if he does something I don't want him to do? Like he spends too much and makes bad investments. He's got no sense about money. Am I just supposed to smile and say nothing?"

"Okay, good, hold that thought. I want each of you to tell me how you felt when Karen said what she just said."

Gary said, "I felt resentful. We were getting along so well here, why'd she have to bring that up?"

I looked at Karen and asked, "As soon as you said that, how did you feel and what crossed your mind?"

"I felt terrible. I knew I shouldn't have said it. I'm sorry, I was stupid. Please, Gary?" And she looked at him for forgiveness.

I said, "Karen you're not stupid. You're like 99% of the people in the world. You're knee-deep in external control. If you use Choice Theory, you'd rarely say anything like that and if you did, you'd have a way to patch it up. What you do when you move to Choice Theory is you stop using the seven deadly habits."

Karen said, "Seven deadly what? What are you talking about?"

"I'm talking about what I call the seven deadly habits of highly miserable people. Keep using that one about money or any of the others and I can guarantee you a lifetime of misery. I think that the deadly habits are one of the main sources of your fibromyalgia. I think any human pain or misery that has no obvious cause is a product of one or more of the deadly habits."

Gary said, "What are they?"

"Before I tell you what they are I want to go a little further into what Karen just said. Gary, tell me, is there a kernel of truth in what she said about how you invest your money?"

"Okay, I made a foolish investment about two years ago and she's never let me forget it."

"Karen, this is important. I want to teach you something about external control that's going to be very hard for you to learn. And I don't mean to single you out. It's not just you. It's Jim, your sister, your mother and father, Gary's mother and father, all mothers and fathers and husbands and wives everywhere. This is a universal truth. Please answer me this. In your mind, who do you think knows more about money, you or Gary?"

"I think I do." Karen replied.

I continued, "Would you say that when it comes to money, you believe you're right and he's wrong."

"I made one lousy investment. We're not in the poorhouse."

"I told you I'm sorry I said it but you know I know more about investing than you do."

"Okay, please, relax. Think about why you're here. I'm trying to help you get rid of these confrontations. Be thankful for what just happened. I think you can learn a lot from it. Look how quickly you both jumped into external control and got all worked up. Why do you think you flared up so fast?"

"She has a better life than she ever dreamed about and she keeps saying I have no sense about money. She never misses a chance to put me down."

"I never miss a chance? That's a good one. He's ticked because for once I got my two cents in before he could shut me up."

"Relax, you both know you can fight. What I'm trying to teach you is how to stop doing what you just did. Think about my question."

Gary said, "What was your question? I forgot."

Karen said, "It was something about flaring up."

"It was about why it happened so fast. It's as if you're both coiled up like snakes waiting for a chance to strike each other. I want to explain why. It'll help if you know why."

It took me a moment to get their attention. Once external control gets going, people forget what they're doing. I began to explain this by saying, "Let me tell you a little story. Early in our lives, when we're about ten, fifteen or twenty years old, we all figure out what the right thing is for us to do and say in most situations when we're trying to get along with people. You know courtesy, waiting your turn, following the rules, picking up your mess, simple knowledge we use every day. And I'm not finding any fault with that; it's a very important part of all our lives. Do you agree with that?"

They both nodded. I noticed Karen had taken Gary's hand again and he was squeezing hers. I went on, "But then, a little later in life almost all of us get kind of an insight. It may be sudden or it may creep in gradually but we almost all get it. That insight goes this way: you say to yourself, 'My goodness, I not only know what's right for me, I know what's right for everybody.' And with that insight, you release the full force of external control into your relationships. The more you know you're right, the more you'll do what you just did. It's what I explained in the last chapter. If it's in our quality world we think it's right. In Karen's quality world she sees herself as knowing a lot about money, more than you do. And you resent it."

Karen said, "I wondered why you were stressing that part about having to be right."

They both waited for me to go on, "This insight, *I know what's right for everybody*, is almost as universal as breathing. It's this insight that adds moral purpose to our behavior. Driven by the belief they're right, people throughout history have committed atrocities beyond belief. It has led men who believe they are right to murder at least a thousand women this year just in this country, alone. When we know we're right, there's almost no limit to our anger, and the war between people goes on and on. Few are spared from this strife as you just demonstrated. But the fact is, few of us are ever completely right or completely wrong. The truth is almost always in between but you'll never find that truth as long as you use external control."

There was a long pause after that speech and then Gary said, "I guess it's a little anticlimactic after that lecture, but tell us, what are the deadly habits?"

"No, it's not anticlimactic at all. Driving the deadly habits out of your marriage or any relationship is the key to all I've been trying to explain. But before I explain them, I have to cover one more thing. Do you believe that we all have a need to love and belong with each other?"

"Something made me forgive Karen when she took my hand and said she was sorry."

"If that need wasn't in me, I'd have left Gary fifteen years ago. I keep holding on because I love him." As she said this she raised his hand and held it again to her chest. There were tears in both their eyes.

"When you fell in love, you wanted to get married. When you did, it was the happiest time of your life. Now let me show you something that really works if, underneath all the bickering, you really love each other. This won't save a loveless marriage but I think it can do a lot for yours. See here in my hand is a piece of magic chalk. You can't see it but it's really there. I'm going to draw a circle on the floor around your chairs. It's just a circle, you're not trapped. Either of you could get up and step out any time you wanted." They watched very carefully as I drew the circle around them.

Then I went back to my chair and said, "I just drew an imaginary circle. I sometimes call it a marriage circle because there are three things in the circle: a husband, a wife, and another entity. It's sitting there right between you, touching both of you. I can almost see it."

They looked at me but didn't know what I was referring to. I then explained, "That entity is your marriage. A husband and a wife are connected by their marriage. Would you accept that?"

Karen said, "We weren't too connected a few minutes ago when we had that blowup." Gary agreed.

"When you had that blowup who got hurt?"

Gary said, "We both did."

Karen said, "I think I get it. Our marriage did. That's what got hurt."

Gary said, "She's right. God, our fighting isn't only killing us, it's killing our marriage."

"That entity, their marriage, is what couples usually forget. Even when you win or seem to win, your marriage always loses. External control doesn't destroy you as individuals. A lot of divorced people do fine by themselves. External control destroys any relationship it can sink its teeth into. And its teeth are the seven deadly habits. Those teeth will chew up and spit out every relationship they get hold of."

They both looked at me for more so I explained, "The habits are like old shoes; ugly, but you're used to wearing them. They were taught to you by your grandparents, your parents, all of your teachers, and most of the people you worked for. The habits destroyed their relationships and they, like you, never really knew what was happening. I'll run through them but don't take notes, you know them as well as the back of your hand. The first, and I believe the most deadly habit is criticizing. That's where you were a few minutes ago. Criticizing is the one that really pops your cork. Then there is blaming. No one likes to hear the words, it's all your fault. After that is complaining. Even if the complainer is not complaining about you, the constant complaints begin to get on your nerves. After that is nagging. Believe me, after you've told someone twenty times to do something, he's heard you. The more you nag, the less chance he'll ever do it. Then threatening and punishing and if they don't work, do it harder. The last, but not least, is rewarding people to control them. In the law it's called bribing. People like the reward but they hate the rewarder. No one likes to be controlled. I referred to them as old shoes because they're so hard to give up. Are you willing to try?"

Gary said, "All of them? Even if I'm really right?"

"Especially if you think you're really right. That's what got to you a few minutes ago. Perhaps you did make a foolish investment but you didn't think so. The criticizing and nagging has hurt your marriage far more than any money you lost."

Karen said to Gary, "He's right. It was the deadly habits that killed our happiness."

Gary said, "Don't use the past tense. They're still killing it. But they're habits, things we do without even thinking. How do we stop doing something we've been doing all our lives?"

"Millions of people have stopped smoking. This isn't as hard as that. There isn't anything that can really replace nicotine, but you can replace the habits with Choice Theory and you don't have to do it all at once. You can do it gradually and apologize when you mess up. You can make a game out of it and win if you give up the habit."

Karen said, "But it still strikes me that, if external control is so bad, why do all of us use it? Like you said, I saw my grandparents and parents fight. You just saw Gary and I fight. Sure we stopped it here but if this'd happened at home we wouldn't have spoken to each other for the rest of the day. We've fought over that investment for a long time."

Gary said, "I don't know, but from what the doctor is saying, I think it has to do with having to be right."

I said, "Being right, that's your need for power talking. Power in a marriage is all external control. You satisfy your need for power by getting the other to give in."

Karen asked, "So how do we get our need for power met? You said that need is in our genes."

"You have to learn that you can still love each other and still admit you're wrong. But not just one of you. Both of you have to be willing to do it. It's called respect. Respect will provide all the power you need in any marriage. The only way I can figure out how to get it is by practicing the golden rule. By really listening to one another, you can have both love and respect."

Gary said, "Could you explain that a little more?"

"First of all, if you respect each other, you accept that your marriage takes precedence over what either of you want. Before Karen said what she did to trigger the old money conflict, she could have asked herself the basic Choice Theory question: Is what I'm about to say good for our marriage? She knew it was bad for it. If you had really listened to one another's needs, respect would have prevented her from saying it. She could even have said to herself, I think I'm right, but if I act on that thought, I know it's going to end in a fight and hurt our marriage. Karen's known the answer to that question for a long time. And I'm not picking on Karen, you've done your share of not respecting her."

"More than my share."

Karen said, "I knew it was wrong but I did it anyway. Why?"

"Because you believed you were right."

"We keep getting back to that right thing, don't we?"

"Choice Theory says we only know what's right for ourselves. And when you're married, the best thing is to always act on what's right for your marriage. But here's another thing I mentioned that may not have registered as strongly as it should. There's one external control behavior you have to avoid at all costs. It makes the deadly habits even more deadly than they usually are."

Gary asked, "What's that?"

"It's using the habits on yourself. That's what I mentioned when I said in the last chapter not to ask too much of yourself and then criticize yourself for not fulfilling all your expectations. If you want to unleash your most harmful creative symptoms, criticizing yourself is the way to do it. Karen may even be criticizing herself for having her illness. It's a common thing for people who have illnesses that doctors can't cure to blame themselves. You can run from others' criticism or pay no attention to them, but you can't get away from yourself."

Karen said, "You're right. Remember the thoughts you referred to that we can not get out of our minds. That's what I do all the time. I kept criticizing myself for what happened to our marriage and then for this illness. The only time I'm able to stop is when I go after Gary. It makes me feel a little better but it wrecks our marriage."

"My experience is that people who have a strong sense of right and wrong often turn against themselves."

Karen said, "Okay. But what do we do if we realize that what we're saying is going to hurt our marriage but we're so angry we say it anyway."

Gary agreed, "We need something to put that control genie back in the bottle as soon as he gets out. We've lived too long with external control; we can't keep him inside that bottle all the time."

"You use the marriage circle and when you do he goes back in. In fact, I also call it a *solving circle* because it's the best place to work on a marriage problem. Why don't we try it right now? Go back to when Karen criticized your financial judgment and try to put that genie back in the bottle. I'll coach you. Karen remember what you said that started it?"

"I said he's got no sense about money."

"Okay, there's the genie. He's out there laughing at you and harming your marriage. But if you're ready to go into the solving circle, we can work on it right now."

Gary said, "What do you mean, if we're ready?" Karen nodded in agreement to his question.

"It means that you're going to try to respect each other by listening and practicing the golden rule. It means that in the circle, you're free to say anything to each other without fear that the other is going to start using the habits."

Karen said, "But doesn't that mean neither of us should use the habits in the circle?"

"You're catching on. In the circle, you're both safe from criticism and anger. Let's see if you can do it. Okay, Karen, you're in the solving circle. What could you say that would help both of you with the problem?"

"As soon as I said it, I'd say, whoops, I'm sorry. I don't want to hurt our marriage."

Gary said, "You'd never say that in a million years if we were alone. You're just trying to impress the doctor."

"Okay, maybe I am. But suppose I really said it. Tell the truth, Gary, what would you say?"

"I wouldn't say anything. I'd be lying on the floor in shock. Oh, I know what I'd say, I'd say, Quick! Call 911."

"See, doctor. There's the real Gary. That's why I'd never say what I just said."

"I'm sorry, Karen. Okay, if you'd actually say something like that once, just once, I'd love it."

I said, "You'd love it and then what would you say?"

"I'd say, let's drop it, it's over. I'm not looking for any more trouble about that investment."

I said. "But you still haven't solved anything. If you drop it, it'll just show up again. Let's actually get in the solving circle and try to solve it instead of just sweeping it back under the rug. Would you like to try?"

Gary said, "How about it, Karen? We have a money problem right now and I'd like to work on it. You know what it is."

"Fine with me and you're damn right I know what it is. But you start. I'm aggravated just thinking about it."

"See, Doctor, she's already aggravated. Is that the way to start?"

"It's okay, the rule in the circle is she doesn't tell you what to do and you don't tell her what to do. But when she says she's aggravated, she's telling you about herself. It's honest. If you weren't both aggravated, you wouldn't be in the circle in the first place. Go ahead and start."

"It's a boat, I want a new boat."

Karen smiled, "That's what I thought. That is a real problem. I've been waiting to see how he was going to bring it up. But okay, we're in the circle, I can still see the chalk line on the floor around us. Go head, Gary, convince me."

I said, "Don't forget that entity, your marriage, sitting right between you. If either of you needs help, that's what I'm here for."

Gary said, "I want a new boat and it's going to cost a lot. I've been afraid to talk with her about it because I knew it was going to end in a fight."

I said, "Not in the solving circle, there's no fighting in the circle. The rule is: as soon as anyone starts a fight, the circle disappears. Go ahead, Gary, it's still there."

"Okay, I'll start with the truth. Karen, I want a new boat. You've known it for a long time. I've been afraid to bring it up. Will you let me explain it without starting in with the habits? Dr. Glasser, would that be a good thing to say at this point?"

"Perfect. The circle has to be safe or it won't work."

Gary said, "I can't believe you're just sitting there after I said, I want a new boat."

"I heard you, honey, this is the new Karen. Go ahead, tell me what's on your mind."

"I think what worries you is we can't afford it. And as long as you're worried about that, you'll never enjoy it. So instead of doing what I've done so many times, I don't plan to just go out and buy it. I'd like to involve you in the whole process so it'll be our boat, not my boat. We'll have to agree on everything every step along the way, including whether we can afford it. The boat is to help our marriage, not hurt it. How does that sound?"

Karen said, "It sounds great to me. I want us to have a new boat, too. I just don't want any surprises. But this seems too easy. Is it going to work?"

I said, "If you both agree along the way like Gary said, it has to work."

Karen added, "But what if I tell you we can't afford the one you want. Are you going to accept that or are you going to nag and nag? It's the nagging that wears me down."

Gary said, "If you'll come along with me through the whole process, I think it can work. Before, I'd know you were going to be angry so I'd just go and buy it anyway. As long as I had to deal with all your anger I'd figure, I may as well have what I want."

Karen said, "I'm not angry. Like I said, I want a new boat, too. If you do what you've just said, I'll respect you more. I know it may be hard for you to believe but I do want to respect you. I think the good doctor has taught a couple of old dogs a new trick."

*****

I'm sure by now you've got the idea. Whenever you improve your relationships you help yourself. Marriage or any relationship is not an "I" thing or a "you" thing. It's a "we" thing and the solving circle is all about reconnecting by focusing on the "we." Keep the "we" in your relationships, get closer to each other, and keep reading this book. If you're saying to yourself right now this sounds too hard to do, then ask yourself this question, is being miserable easier?

7

Women Not in an Intimate Relationship

efore I go further, I want to remind readers that I am not claiming Choice Theory will cure fibromyalgia. But if enough of you get relief from what I suggest here, it will indicate I'm on the right track. Again, I want to stress that learning Choice Theory is perfectly safe. You don't have to do anything except start dealing with the people in your life differently. There is no diet, exercise, medication or mandatory medical test(s). As much as you are not now in control of your symptoms, you are in complete control of everything suggested in this book. If your relationships get better, I believe you'll be happier.

After the meeting with Karen and Gary, I wrote Chapter Six and sent it for comments. They called me a week later and said they were delighted with the chapter. In fact, since our meeting, they'd been using what they learned and were getting along very well. As you may have guessed, Karen and Gary are not their real names and the problem they tackled in the solving circle had to do with finances but was not a boat.

About a week after that I got a call from Karen asking if Ellen, the single mother from Chapter Four, was a real person. I told her she wasn't. She was a composite of many single mothers with problem teenagers I had counseled or taught over the years. I felt safe in using her because I'm sure there are many divorced women with difficult teenagers who've been diagnosed with fibromyalgia. Because I don't like to deal in abstractions when I explain Choice Theory, I brought Ellen to life in Chapter Four so readers could see how the combination of total behavior and unhappy relationships may explain their pain and disability.

I asked Karen why she wanted to know about Ellen. She said, "I've become very friendly with a single mother of a fifteen-year-old girl who goes to the same school as our kids. I'd noticed that occasionally she carries a cane and, once in a while, she'd seen me with my four-pronger. It didn't take us long to get acquainted and discover we'd both read the article in the *New Yorker*. I hope you don't mind, but I told her about you and your book and pointed out that you'd written about a woman named Ellen in Chapter Four who fit her to a tee. She asked if what I'd learned has done any good. I told her I do feel better but it's too soon to really tell. With this diagnosis, anything new you do seems to help for a while. But when I told her that Gary and I are definitely getting along better and that we are even using your theory with our kids and getting some relief, she got really interested. Do you see why I'm calling?"

"You want to share what I've written with her."

"Is it okay? I told her that Gary and I were in the book. Can I give her what we have for her to read?"

"Sure go ahead, it's fine with me. The more people who learn about Choice Theory, the better. I've been looking for some feedback from a woman who isn't in an intimate relationship. That's a very different situation from what you have."

"I think it's tougher. At least Gary and I have each other."

"If you give it to her and she likes it, tell her I'd love to talk with her and maybe put her experience with it in the book, too. I'll disguise her. No one would ever know who she was."

Sure enough, it took about six weeks before a woman called and told me she was the "Ellen" who Karen knew from school. She told me her real name but I told her if I wrote up what we talked about I'd continue to use the names Ellen and Samantha. She said, she'd gotten into what I'd written and she'd like very much to talk. It turned out that the following Saturday was fine for both of us. She was carrying her cane when I opened the door and explained. "I don't always need it but I feel better if I have it with me."

Ellen was about the same age as Karen. But unlike Karen, she was painfully thin. Her face was pinched as if she were in pain but I could see she'd be very attractive if she gained a few pounds and could get rid of the expression on her face. I couldn't help noticing how beautifully dressed she was; blouse, skirt, and pale yellow cashmere sweater, all selected to complement each other and go well with her light brown hair. She seemed a little unsure of herself and I asked her if she was uncomfortable because of anything she'd read.

"I was angry at first. Karen had warned me I would be, you know, about your claim that I'm choosing the pain. I guess I read parts of Chapter Four a dozen times before I simmered down and pretty much accepted that I have no control over the feeling and the physiology components of my total behavior. If you want to know if what you wrote is clear, I'd be happy to take a test on the book. I'm sure I'd pass; I practically memorized it. What you say makes a lot of sense but it's hard to accept that I've been doing a lot of harm to myself and the people close to me since I was a teenager."

"What do you mean?"

"The deadly habits. You know, doing the right thing. My God, no one's ever been more gifted with knowing what's right for others than I have."

"I guess you really got into Chapters Four and Six. How about the other chapters, like Chapter Five?"

"After reading that chapter, the thought of living on the street was almost appealing, compared to this. Seriously, I'm already beyond the book. I went out and bought *Choice Theory* and read it thoroughly. I don't have any of that fibrofog they mentioned in Groopman's article. Some of the chapters I read twice, like Chapters Four, Seven and Nine, especially Nine. In that chapter, you call me Linda and I have headaches instead of fibromyalgia, but my daughter's name is the same in both books. Do you have some kind of thing for the name Samantha?"

"I stole that case from my own book but I'd forgotten the names. Could you relate to Linda, her headaches and the problems with her Samantha?"

"Relate to her, it was uncanny! We both have good jobs and we're both external control freaks. The main difference is her daughter did well in school and liked it.

My daughter hates school with a passion. She won't do any homework and just scrapes by. But the outcome is similar. Linda learned to get along with her Samantha and I'm getting along much better with my daughter now that I've decided to get off her back. It's her life. I can't control her. I got her some birth control pills and hope for the best. The good part is that for the last month we're almost back to where we were when she was twelve. All that stuff about external control killing relationships, you're sure right there."

"I sense you're here today to talk to me about something other than Samantha."

"I am. I don't think Samantha has much to do with my fibromyalgia. It started while we were still getting along well. Actually it has to do with me, the way I picture myself. But it also has to do with my ex. I can't seem to get him out of my head. Oh, I guess I should now say, out of my quality world. We've been divorced for seven years and I still miss him. The control freak in me drove him to another woman but he's still stuck inside my head. Karen's lucky. She's not nearly as controlling as I am, that's why she's still with Gary. But I'll tell you, your Choice Theory has helped them. She keeps telling me how different her life is from the way it was. But my husband's gone. It's too late for me with him."

"The reason he's still in your quality world is you haven't made any real effort to replace him. To get him out you need to consider putting someone else in."

"That's easy for you to say. Like good men grow like fruit on trees waiting to be picked by forty-three-year-old skeletons. See how I am, I come here for help and the first thing I do is attack you. I may be the first fatality from this disease."

"Relax, I'm a psychiatrist, I can't afford to get hurt by what people say. You're up front so we'll get along just fine. It's not easy for me to say what I said to you and I wish I could have answered your question without saying it. But I don't think he's as stuck in your quality world as you do. Keeping him in there is easier than facing another problem that's much harder to face. My guess is it's the problem that's connected with your fibromyalgia. I think you're aware of the problem. Could you tell me what it is? I'd rather you tell me than for me to guess. But if you want me to, I'll tell you what I think and if it'll help, I think there's a Choice Theory solution for that problem, too."

There was a long pause. She was thinking. I pushed her for the problem because I recognized that Ellen is a strong woman. You have to be both strong and creative even to have this diagnosis. If we can get it out on the table, I think we can solve it. I also want to explain that what I'm doing now is psychotherapy even though I promised in the book I'd only teach. I'm doing this little bit of therapy because I need to explain an important Choice Theory point and this is the quickest way to get there. What she then said is what I'm sure was going through the minds of quite a few of the suffering women gathered at the Westin Hotel.

Ellen had no trouble reading my mind. She said, "I just can't accept I'm going to be alone the rest of my life. But I've never been able to relate to a man in a way that lasts. Here I am, forty-three-years old and I've given up on even looking for the love I know I need. I know I've given up because look at me, I'm so thin it's ridiculous. I try to eat but I've no appetite. Samantha calls me anorexic. I think she's right. And remember those thoughts you can't get out of your head, the ones your creativity shoves into your consciousness. Here's one of mine. Every time I look at my food, my creativity attacks me by saying, 'Why eat? Who's ever going to want you?' Things are better now with Samantha but still no let up in the pain. Well... I can't say that completely. I do feel better since we've been getting along... Look, I'm glad you're a psychiatrist. It feels good to tell this to someone who has a chance of understanding what I'm talking about and doesn't get bent out of shape by everything I say."

When she finished telling me that, she looked at me as if to challenge my contention that there's a Choice Theory answer to her problem. I said, "Ellen you've learned an amazing amount of my theory in a very short time but to help you solve your problem I want to teach you a little more. There's no reason for you to be alone the rest of your life. What I think you've missed in your study of Choice Theory is the power in the word *choice*. The external control world we live in, with all its pressure to do what we're told or suffer the consequences, has convinced most of us to believe we have far fewer choices than we actually have. Remember how uncomfortable you were when I suggested, even indirectly in the book, that you might be choosing your pain?"

"I was more than uncomfortable, I was angry."

"Angry at me?"

"Yes, angry at you. Even when I finally realized that I didn't directly choose the pain, I was still uncomfortable. This whole idea of choice and choosing is hard to accept."

"Suppose I told you that if you could directly choose your pain as easily as you choose your actions and thoughts, you'd be better off."

"I'd say now you've really gone off the deep end."

"Maybe, but tell me, what do the words *choice* or *choosing* mean to you?"

"They mean what they say. That I have options, like I'm choosing to sit here and talk to you."

"Could you choose to get up now and leave or to sit there and start to whistle, *Dixie*?"

"Okay, there're lots of things I could do. I get the point."

"If your pain were directly chosen, just like you're choosing to sit in that chair, wouldn't you be better off than now? Or would you be better off if it weren't chosen; if you had no control over that pain at all, no control over whether it comes or goes?"

Ellen was a very perceptive woman. Immediately, she said, "I get the point. Of course, I'd be better off to have control over the pain even if I chose to have it. But I don't have control or I wouldn't be here. Are you implying there's some way for me to get control of it?"

"No, not that I know of. I wish there were. But please, follow along with me and you'll see where I'm going. Let's go back to the way Samantha was a year ago."

"God forbid."

"No, please, this is just conjecture. A year ago you were grounding her and getting nowhere. Did you believe when you were grounding her that you had another viable choice?"

"No… I felt totally stuck."

"Tell me, you've made another choice, you said you're getting along a lot better. What are you actually choosing to do that seems to be working for you with her?"

"As soon as I got off her back, things improved. Instead of fighting over a curfew, I gave her my cellular when she went out and asked her to call me from wherever she was by eleven o'clock and tell me when she'd be home. For awhile it was rocky, but I didn't criticize or punish. I just kept asking and now she's calling every time she goes out. Maybe not exactly at eleven, but close. Sometimes if she's going to be extra late she calls again to let me know. Just that simple request has kept my concern for her in her mind without taking away her freedom. It tells her I trust her. Actually, I had to trust her or never let her leave the house. Then when she comes home, no matter how late it is, and it's been getting earlier every week for the past month, I make sure we talk. I ask her to tell me anything that went on that she thinks I'll find interesting, but not to feel that she has to tell me everything. She snuggles in with me as soon as she gets home and we talk until we both fall asleep. Some of the things she tells me I don't want to know but the closeness we now have feels so good that I think it's kind of protecting her. Before, she was so angry I was worried she'd do things to spite me. Just getting rid of the deadly habits has made them unnecessary. What you said to Karen and Gary, 'If it's going to drive you apart don't say it,' was good advice for them and for me, too. All this helps but it also hurts, if you know what I mean. I feel better with Samantha but that feeling better makes me even more acutely aware of my own loneliness."

"What would you have said six months ago if I'd told you you'd be snuggled down in bed with Samantha after she came home from a date?"

"I'd have said you were crazy."

"What would you say now if I told you that your chances of finding a man to replace your ex in your quality world are very slim? It may never happen."

"That's what I believe, I told you that."

"I'm not asking what you believe. I want you to answer my question, I'll repeat it: what would you say if I told you that your chances of finding a man to replace your ex are very slim? Just say something; try to answer that question. I'm not claiming there's a good answer but there's an answer."

"Do you want me to tell you my life is over?"

"Please Ellen, I don't want you to tell me anything. I asked a question and I'd like you to answer it. I'm sure you can come up with something."

"Is this therapy? Are you trying to get me to tell you I won't kill myself?"

"You're stubborn, aren't you? Take your time, I'll wait."

"Okay, I don't know if this is what you want but I'm not going to kill myself. I mean I've thought about it but I'd never do that to my daughter. And I would never hurt her either, though, believe me, there were times when that thought also crossed my mind."

"I didn't ask you to tell me what you're not going to do. I want you to tell me what you are going to do."

There was some exasperation in her voice when she said, "I'm not going to do anything. I'm going to do what I've been doing for the past seven years since he left."

"Please, don't think I'm being smart but, for me to teach you the Choice Theory I think you need to know, I want to correct what you just said."

"Go ahead and correct me. I'm enjoying this conversation."

"If you want to get the full power of Choice Theory, you'd have said, I'm going to *choose* to do what I've been doing for the past seven years since he left. Just add the word choose, that's all."

"But I don't choose to do those things... Okay, okay, maybe I do."

"Don't worry about it, I say the same thing once in a while. We all do. For the past seven years you've been choosing your actions and most of your thoughts. I know your creative system intervenes with a few thoughts once in a while. You also chose to talk to Karen and you chose to read all you've read. And you chose to come here because you thought that would be a good thing to do. You've chosen every word you've uttered since you came into this office. And you're going to choose all your actions and almost all your thoughts for the rest of your life whether you find anyone to replace your ex or not."

"But if I keep doing what I've been doing, I'm going to be miserable."

"You're going to choose to be miserable?"

"No, no, damn it. I don't choose my feelings, I only choose my thoughts and actions. I read that chapter. I told you I read the part about what I choose a dozen times."

"Are you choosing to be angry now?"

There was a long pause. She was really fighting to restrain her anger. Then she relaxed and smiled and with a voice like the cat swallowing the canary said, "No, I'm choosing to think that you're pointing out that I'm a damn fool and I was angry at you for having the gall to point it out. I was still hoping you'd take pity on me and say you're sorry for all the suffering I've been through."

"Good teachers don't feel sorry if their students are a little slow; they just keep teaching. I'm trying to teach you that you choose all your thoughts and actions even if you know that pain and misery are going to go along with those thoughts and actions. I'm trying to teach you that every choice we just talked about is no harder to make than what you did with Samantha. We can all make better choices but we can't make them if we don't believe they're choices. That's the whole point of Choice Theory. You always have choices. You can choose to live the next seven years a lot better than the last seven years. If you don't like how you feel, you can change how you think and act. It's your life. I'm not trying to change it. I'm choosing to teach you some new ideas so you can get more control over your life."

"I'm sorry I cursed."

"I'm glad you did, it helped me teach and your anger helped you pay attention, didn't it?"

"Okay, I choose everything but can't I get help? Am I all on my own?"

"Sure you can get help but, in the end, it's always your choice. A lot of people may help by offering you suggestions, but steer clear of people who tell you what to do. You know about those people, you've been one of them for thirty years. In fact, I'd like to make a suggestion right now."

"What do you suggest?"

"I suggest you start eating so you don't have to look at yourself in the mirror and see a scarecrow."

"Sounds good. How about if I could maybe, just maybe, choose to stop thinking about my ex and start thinking about getting a life?"

"I'm sure Samantha would agree with that. Can I make one more suggestion?"

"Go ahead."

"When you talk to Karen, ask her if she'd like to get together with you once in a while and talk over how you're doing without the deadly habits. If she hasn't read it, you might share with her what you learned from reading *Choice Theory*."

"Good suggestion, but I think we've already got that started."

She was smiling when she left the office. Her face had lost its pinched look and we both felt good.

8

Sue's Story

Although I have an office that takes care of all the William Glasser Institute work and also helps me in scheduling my frequent lecture trips, I work at home. Linda, who runs the Institute, comes to my home about once a week to consult on Institute business. The rest of the time I am in close touch with the office by phone, fax and e-mail. As soon as I read Dr. Groopman's article in the *New Yorker*, I began to work on this book at home. By the time I finished the fourth chapter it occurred to me that Sue, who has worked in our office for over eleven years, might be able to help me personally with what I was writing.

I remember Linda telling me that for several years Sue had some undiagnosed sickness that so incapacitated her that she finally became unable to work. But then she began to recover and in the last three years has returned to work, slowly at first, but now for three days a week. This is all she wants to work and she's so efficient that we do with what she can give us. I wondered if her sickness might be fibromyalgia, except she seemed to be doing so much better now than the women in the article. I talked to Linda, whom I knew had been doing all she could to help Sue, and asked Linda to read Dr. Groopman's article. If Linda agreed that the article might be helpful to Sue, I wanted her to ask Sue to read it and tell me what she thought.

Sue was not only interested in the article, she was very interested in what I was writing, so when I finished the previous seven chapters, I shared them with her. I then talked to Sue and her husband, Jeff, and they told me about her illness. Her story was so congruent with what I believed she and any other sufferers needed to do if they were to help themselves that I asked her if she'd write about her experiences leading up to the diagnosis and how she was doing now. The following is what she wrote:

Sue's Story

When I first read Dr. Groopman's article and then Dr. Glasser's manuscript, I could see how the ideas corresponded with my situation. I told him that I really wished I had had the information in this book when I was so ill. It is my hope that my story might be able to help others living with fibromyalgia.

I really can't remember a significant incident in my life that brought on the fibromyalgia. I've read a couple of books that speculate that it might be caused by the onset of an infection or traumatic incident such as a car accident. Maybe this is so, but after reading this book, I also believe that Dr. Glasser's approach is much more applicable to my own situation.

After being together for three years, my husband, Jeff, and I married in 1987. With my parents' help, we bought our first home the same year. This was followed by the birth of my second son, David, in 1988. My oldest son, Michael, was six and Jeff was the perfect stepfather for him. We shared custody of Michael with his father, Evan. Everything was coming together. We were young, happy, and building the life I'd always dreamed of.

When David was six weeks old, I started back working for my father, an attorney who at that time practiced out of his home. I really wanted to stay home and be a fulltime mother, but couldn't afford to, so I had to find outside daycare for David. We were very fortunate to locate an older couple who truly loved David, but I struggled with not being able to stay home with him myself.

After my father retired in 1989, I tried working at home doing word processing, but the income was small and unsteady. It was time to go out and find a job. So, in 1989, I interviewed with Linda, and began working part-time at The William Glasser Institute. Michael was now seven and David was one-and-a-half. I started out part-time so I could be there for my children. This job was different from any others I'd had. I read Dr. Glasser's books and took a deep interest in the work of the Institute.

Jeff and I had a great relationship and spent every minute together we could. We both shared the love of the outdoors and would enjoy taking our boys out hiking in the mountains. We'd take a lot of mini vacations. The boys loved to fish, so we'd rent a little boat and go out on the water. We had many friends with children and spent lots of time with them doing family things. The kids went everywhere we went and we all had so much fun together.

Michael and David meant the world to me. My number one job was being a mom.

We live in a small, comfortable home in Chatsworth. We had lots of children on the block. I felt like the neighborhood mom as we always had kids in the house. Sometimes I'd set up little art projects for the kids to do. The two girls from next door were over so much that Michael was beginning to think he had sisters.

I spent lots of time keeping the house looking just right. My husband compared my behavior to that of a housefly. I just didn't sit still. There was just always something that needed to be done. My friends would say I did my housework with a toothbrush. A toothbrush? Well maybe, just in the corners. I just wanted my perfect family and my perfect house. It was just the way I was.

In 1990, when Michael was about nine, his fourth grade teacher called and asked if we could talk. She told me that Michael had told her about some very disturbing things that were going on in his father's home. Evan had married, his wife had left him, and he was now living with his girlfriend. Unfortunately, we did not have a good relationship with Michael's father. He seldom worked and heavily relied on his mother for financial support. Up until now, we had shared joint legal and physical custody with Evan. But with this information from Michael's teacher, we knew we had to try to gain full custody of Michael. Jeff and I had been to court before. We had deep concerns about his father's lifestyle, but without proof our hands were tied.

This time we proved to the court that we could provide a more stable environment for Michael and in 1991, we were able to gain full custody. However, the stress of a child custody suit was overwhelming. Evan's family took care of his lawyer fees but Jeff and I had to pay out thousands of dollars from our own pockets. A court-ordered psychiatrist visited our home on three occasions. Dr. Glasser's ideas helped me greatly during this time in dealing with Evan's allegations, which simply weren't true. I knew that although I had no control over what he presented to the court, I did have control over how I presented myself.

Evan was very unhappy and it seemed to us like he did everything he could to make our lives miserable. I believed that he abused drugs and alcohol but without proof, couldn't stop his court-ordered visitations. I worried constantly about him taking his anger out on Michael. The stress was unbearable. My heart would just ache when Michael had to go to Evan's home. I spent a lot of time stressing about Evan's time with him. I wanted to do what was best for him, so in 1991, when Michael was nine, I enrolled him in his first season of Little League. He started off as the star pitcher. He had never played baseball, but it turned out he was really good. The first season Evan volunteered as assistant coach. I was the Team Mom. It was an awkward situation. I guess I had pictured that this would be an activity for our family. I felt that Evan was interfering in that and it really bothered me.

In 1992, along with my husband, we took a Basic Intensive Week in Reality Therapy and the theory on which it is based. Along with this training I read many of Dr. Glasser's books including the book called *Control Theory,* which was the precursor to Dr. Glasser's book, *Choice Theory*. I learned I couldn't control Evan's behavior, just my own. I'd done what I could and that was it.

Life was very busy. I was now working 35 hours a week at the Institute, seven hours a day. This enabled me to get Michael to his baseball practices and games on time. I knew other women did a great job of juggling work and family, but it didn't seem to come easy to me. As crazy as life was, I began thinking about having another baby. I was twenty-nine and I think that's about the time my biological clock started ticking. Jeff wanted more children, too. But to pay for a babysitter would mean we'd have to put David in public school when he started kindergarten. Because of a trust fund left by Michael's grandparents, he had always had the benefit of attending private school and we wanted that for David, too. So, we put the idea of having another baby on hold. In Choice Theory terms, what I wanted, I couldn't have.

It was about this time in 1992 that I started becoming sick. I began catching colds constantly. Then the colds would go into my lungs, not as an infection, but more as a severe, almost untreatable, allergy. Several times I had to go to the hospital for intravenous steroid drips. But even with the steroids I began to have severe allergic reactions. My whole body would itch and my face would swell up. I developed rashes that covered me from head to toe. These allergy attacks continued for several years. The doctors put me on Prednisone still not knowing what I was reacting to. At this time I was also starting to feel very exhausted and at times would have a lot of pain in my neck and shoulders.

The doctors didn't have an answer to the pain and fatigue, so they concentrated on the physical symptoms of my allergies. I was referred to an allergist, followed by over a year of allergy shots, two days a week. But the shots didn't seem to rid me of the constant aches and fatigue. I'm not even sure it did much for my allergies. If anything, going in for the shots was just adding to my continually busy schedule.

I couldn't get the idea out of my head that more than anything I wanted to be a stay-at-home mom. Other mothers in our neighborhood stayed home. Why couldn't I? Of course, bringing this idea up to Jeff wasn't a happy subject. Jeff is a very hard worker. He's worked for a telecommunications company since he was eighteen years old. His typical day is usually 10 hours, but frequently he has to work on cable outages that keep him out all night. Because we had a second mortgage on the house from building a third bedroom after David was born and, of course, many other bills, we just couldn't handle things on one income. I was working full time when we bought the house and our lifestyle was just geared to two incomes.

But still, sometimes I would get mad at Jeff. I was always the "saver" and he was the "spender," although we really just didn't have a lot of extra money to spend. I never asked for help around the house. I was supposed to be the perfect wife and mother and believed it was my job. I don't think Jeff or the kids ever said to themselves, "Gee, look at this shower. It needs scrubbing. I think I'll do that while I take a shower. I'll even scrub the toilet on the way out." No, that's never happened. I was twenty years old when I met Jeff, and Michael was two. It was so important to me to be the perfect housewife. I had always kept the house clean and cooked big dinners. I took my role as a wife and mother very seriously.

So I continued with my busy life, up at 5:30 getting ready for work and my morning drive. I made sure the kids had a hot breakfast and a good sack lunch for school. After work, Michael usually had a game or practice, so we were off to the ball field. I really loved watching his games. Jeff would meet us there and it was really fun. But I didn't feel like I fit in with those fancy, private school, baseball moms. Oh, they were nice enough, but I felt so jealous of them. How easy it was for them with their diamonds and SUVs. They didn't have to go to work every day or scrub floors. I listened to them complain about their husbands, about how putting the Olympic-size pool in was ruining their flowers, how they barely had time to lunch with the girls or make it to the gym three times a week. They had it so easy. Wait a minute! I'm not a mean or envious person, am I? We do okay. Anyway, after the games, it was time to get dinner started, pick up clothes off the floor and get the laundry in. I felt like I did laundry around the clock. I also spent every minute I could helping the kids with their homework and reports. I wanted them to do well in school. I knew this would give them the self-confidence needed to later succeed in life. They did very well and made us proud by bringing home terrific grades. By the time I finally sat down to rest, I was so exhausted I'd usually just go to bed.

Jeff and I really were not spending as much time together as we used to. It wasn't that we didn't want to, but we were always just so busy. I was irritable at times and Jeff would think I was mad at him. I think I was just becoming angry with my life. I started missing out on a lot of the fun activities so I could make time to take care of the housework.

By now, both kids had dirt bikes and one of my favorite activities was to drive out to the mountains with Jeff and the kids on Saturday. They'd ride their dirt bikes and I would dole out sandwiches. It was beautiful there and I enjoyed it a lot. I even tried riding the dirt bike once, but no one told me there was a brake. I just assumed if you let up off the gas, it would stop. Needless to say, that was the end of my motorcycle career! After a while, however, I began to tell Jeff to go ahead without me. I had to catch up on the grocery shopping and clean the house. Oh, and I'd better get out there and clean up the dog poop. Jeff didn't worry about how clean the house was or if there was enough food for the lunches tomorrow. He always made time for fun. I wondered how he could be so carefree. I worried about everything.

During these years there were several other issues going on. Problems arise and you have to deal with them. There was the 1994 Northridge Earthquake. Thankfully, none of us was hurt; however, with no earthquake insurance, we had to bear the costs of many repairs to our home. Jeff and I also had to deal with the constant strain of Michael's father who had undergone back surgery and become addicted to prescription drugs. One of the baseball moms witnessed Evan taking pills, drinking a lot of beer at a baseball dinner, and then leaving to drive Michael home.

I asked the mom to write me a letter to show to the courts, but she refused. She said she was scared Evan would retaliate. His behavior became more and more off-the-wall. He would call us in the middle of the night and say things like, "The Cuban government is after me." He would become quite detailed with his delusions. When he would call Michael during the day and start talking this way, Michael would usually just shrug and hand me the telephone.

I tried to tell the court investigator what was going on. But again, other than hearing some of Evan's telephone conversations with Michael, which didn't stand up in court, we didn't have the proof that was needed. Michael was about twelve or thirteen now and understood Evan had problems. He began refusing to go to his father's home every other weekend. Michael's aunt, however, fixed the situation by having Evan and Michael stay with her on those weekends.

Evan would show up for many of Michael's ball games. I knew it shouldn't bother me, but I let it anyway. I realized I couldn't keep him away from the baseball field, but really wished he would stick to his court-ordered visitation. We never asked for child support because we thought Evan would make Michael feel bad about it. Not that he could have paid anyway; he was living on disability.

By this time, I was becoming increasingly tired and I'd think, what's wrong with me? I started declining invitations to socialize. I just wasn't feeling well.

In April of 1995, when Michael was only thirteen, Evan died from a drug overdose. I couldn't bring myself to tell Michael the cause of his father's death, although he found out years later from a relative. To make matters worse, the day Evan died just happened to be my birthday. Now Michael would forever have to deal with his mom's birthday being a reminder of his father's death. I was so angry with Evan. How could he have put us through so much? Why hadn't he been a better father to Michael?

The very next month, after a nine-month illness, one of my dearest friends died from cancer. I spent as much time with him as I could, but there was nothing anyone could do. The surgery and pain he went through were unbearable. I felt so useless. I really had to make an effort just to spend time with him. I was just so tired. How come my health was so bad? If anything, you'd think that I'd toughen up to deal with life's issues.

By now, I hurt all over and felt so tired all of the time, I could barely function. The doctors still didn't have an answer for the pain and fatigue. I was having a difficult time driving. My arms hurt so much that even turning the wheel was painful. I felt like I was in a fog and I wasn't really part of the same world everyone else was. It was like the fibrofog Dr. Groopman referred to in his article. My nights were getting worse. My legs would twitch and I would toss and turn, waking up anywhere from 1:00 to 3:00 a.m. and not being able to fall back to sleep. Even when I did sleep, I would dream constantly. Some nights I couldn't sleep at all. This would make my increasingly rotten days even harder to deal with. Still, I tried to keep up with my busy life. I felt that I had no choice. Thinking back on it now, I was resenting all that was expected of me and all that I expected of myself.

It was getting more difficult to work. I'd sit at my desk but it was hard to deny the terrible pain I was in. I would take Tylenol every four hours for days at a time. Sometimes when people would talk to me, it was like I couldn't comprehend what they were saying. My back and arms ached so much it was hard to concentrate on anything but the pain. I tried to keep most of it to myself but when you feel like you have the flu most of the time, it is difficult to talk about much else. I don't think people understood how I was feeling. Other than my eyes looking tired, there weren't any other physical changes. How I wished that someone could spend a day in my body so I could convince them of how badly I felt.

The mornings were the worst. When I would finally force myself out of bed, I literally had to walk hunched over because the pain in my back and shoulders was so bad. Even my legs and feet hurt. There were days where

I'd sit at my chair applying my make-up trying to hold the tears back long enough to get my eyeliner just right. Many times I would be nauseous. I was so mad at Jeff. Didn't he see what hell I was going through? I knew he didn't have anything to do with how bad I felt, but I was mad at him anyway.

When Michael was about fifteen, one of his friends told me he was hanging around with a bad crowd at school. It wasn't long after that he got into trouble and was expelled. We had little choice but to enroll him in the area public high school. Even though he joined the baseball team, he started getting into all kinds of trouble. Here he was a star ball player whose athletic achievements were written up in the paper numerous times. I wondered what was happening to my precious child, my golden boy whom everyone liked. He had such big plans for his life with college and baseball. He had even volunteered as an assistant sports coach at the summer camp he and David attended every summer. So what was he doing?

I would have long talks with him. I used what I learned from Dr. Glasser's books. I would ask questions like "Is what you are doing getting you closer to or further away from what you want?" He knew the answer but he would tell me he just couldn't help himself. Jeff and I started taking him to counseling. After several sessions, the counselor told us not to worry so much. Michael was just going through his difficult teen years.

I continued to be concerned about Michael's behavior. I would literally shake from worry but I just didn't have the energy to deal with this. I couldn't even think straight. I started noticing that when I would get especially upset with Michael, my condition would worsen. Sometimes I would have to go to bed for two or three days at a time.

Back in 1989, when I first read Dr. Glasser's book, *Control Theory*, I couldn't believe how much sense it made. It showed me how much power people had. It taught me that most of the mistakes I'd made in the past were all related to the bad choices I'd made. What a powerful lesson! However, as much as I tried believing that the way I was feeling was somehow a choice, it was almost impossible. Maybe if I had understood more about Dr. Glasser's ideas on how our creative systems work (as he writes in this book), it would have been more clear. But still, knowing what I did about the theory, I knew there must be something under my control to make myself feel better.

I started by searching for answers from my doctor. Over and over I would tell him that this pain and exhaustion weren't normal. Something was wrong with me. Over and over they'd draw blood, call me up and say "everything is normal, you're fine." One time Jeff came with me, I guess to further try to convince the doctor that I wasn't making this up. He related that unless I was up doing laundry or something, I spent most of my time in bed.

The doctor talked mostly to Jeff about working out and how important it was for us to stay healthy at this time in our lives so we could enjoy retirement. He then turned to me and asked, "Are you exercising?" There I sat, slouched over in the chair in that doctor's office, my head in a fog and my eyes sunken and burning. I felt like saying, "Yeah right. I'll just start training for a marathon!"

Once I tested positive for the Epstein Barr virus. I was so happy that someone had found something. My happiness didn't last long when I learned there was nothing I could do about this virus. But surely there was something I could do. This had been going on for so long and seemed to be getting worse. I didn't know how much longer I could endure feeling this way. I started keeping a calendar putting an unhappy face on the days I felt really bad. On the days I felt just okay, I'd draw a happy face. I'd also list the things I'd eaten and the weather. I wanted to know if somehow my worse days corresponded with the temperature or my diet, but it didn't do any good. I simply couldn't find any correlation. All I saw was months turning into years of unhappy faces.

I realized that I just couldn't continue to do everything I was doing. I approached Linda about cutting my hours from thirty-five a week to twenty-eight and a half. I wasn't sure how Linda would deal with this. I had a lot of responsibilities at the Institute, but we'd always had a good relationship so I was hoping she would understand. She did and agreed with my new schedule immediately.

I thought this was the answer to everything. I could pick my David up on time instead of putting him in after-school care, which I had always felt guilty about. I could be home more often with Michael. I was sure I'd feel much better now that I had more time to rest. It was like I had tunnel vision. I focused all my energy on getting everything done so I could rest. This wasn't getting me anywhere.

The next thing I did was to change my diet. I became a vegetarian: absolutely no meat, not even fish or chicken. I even began taking herbal remedies, but this wasn't the answer. My pain and fatigue didn't stop. I believe now that altering my diet to this extent probably made things worse, not better.

Again, I went to Linda. I told her I just wasn't feeling well and it was becoming almost impossible to work. Actually, it was hard to do anything; even sit through a baseball game. Maybe I just needed to get away for a while and think. She thought that perhaps a trip might do me good, so she gave me time off to go visit a friend in Indiana. "Okay," I thought, "this is it. No dishes, no ball games, and no work. I'm sure I'll get rested and feel much better." Except for a couple of out-of-town Institute conferences that I had helped Linda with, I had never spent a night away from my family. I felt so guilty but also knew I had to do something. I was desperate. My trip was nice, but my friends definitely noticed I wasn't the same person they knew before they moved. My energy was low. I didn't want to go out at night at all.

I returned home glad that I'd gone, but still as exhausted as ever. Jeff later told me that when I went to Indiana, he was afraid I wouldn't come back. Did he think I would really ever leave him and the kids? How scary to think that things were so bad.

I spent a lot of time dwelling on how miserable I was. Jeff and I really never spent much fun time together anymore. I was always too tired or too sore to do anything with him. I really thought I had some rare disease that had yet to be diagnosed. I was pretty sure I was dying. But Jeff was always there for me, usually rubbing my back and trying to help me deal with my pain. I think he was frustrated that he wasn't able to help me more. Michael was in deep pain and I couldn't do anything to help him. I worried about David. He had always been a happy child who was close to Michael. But with things becoming increasingly difficult with Michael's problems and my health, I was concerned that David was feeling the stress.

One day my husband was on the Internet. He was searching for something that could explain why his once so energetic wife was now a tired, sore and depressed woman. He brought home articles on chronic-fatigue syndrome and fibromyalgia. This was it. My symptoms fit to a tee.

Armed with this new information, I went back to my doctor, with Jeff by my side. The doctor said, "Sure, I'm aware of fibromyalgia, but there's no cure for it." Did this doctor know what I had all along, but just didn't want to give me a diagnosis because he either knew little about this disease or didn't believe in it? I was so angry. Here I'd been coming to him for years describing my symptoms. Couldn't he have at least mentioned fibromyalgia?

At a loss, my doctor referred me to a rheumatologist. Again, Jeff went with me. We both explained to the doctor what was going on. After talking for about half an hour, he took me into the examining room, gave me the pressure point test and it was textbook positive. He came right to the diagnosis of fibromyalgia. Finally, my misery had a name. Feeling exhausted, no longer able to cope with work, the doctor put me on disability.

This was wonderful. Now I finally got to admit to the world that I was so sick I couldn't even be a productive person. Linda, always understanding, was now put under the pressure of taking on my workload. I felt like a failure to my kids, my husband and now to the job where I was treated so well. I thought to myself, "I might just as well die. Jeff could always remarry and find a better mother for my kids."

The new doctor put me on an antidepressant and a medication to help me sleep. I didn't understand why he would put me on an antidepressant. I was never depressed before I became sick. And, working for Dr. Glasser for so many years, I believed that these drugs might be harmful. I tried taking the antidepressant, but it made me sick to my stomach, and up to now, my stomach was the only thing that didn't hurt! The medication for sleep knocked me out so deeply I felt drugged. On another visit to the rheumatologist, he told me that unless I started taking the medication, he couldn't treat me. So once again I tried. I started with a quarter of a pill for sleeping and a third of the antidepressant. I did believe that the one medication was helping me sleep, so I continued taking it. But the antidepressant didn't seem to improve anything. I was still in a fog.

After being off of work for about six weeks, I started back not much better off than when I'd left. I finally made the decision to quit. I knew I could have probably gone back on disability, but I didn't want that for the Institute and struggled with a picture of myself as a "disabled" person. I had always been able to work. What was I going to do now? Jeff was stressed to the hilt. I knew that somehow I had to bring in some income. What could I do? I contacted an old friend of mine and he said I could help him with his lotion-selling business and I could do most of this from home. Even better, I didn't have to think too much, which was good because of my brain fog.

Oh well, it was something. Jeff and I would label bottles, put together gift baskets, and then drive out to Ventura to get them on the cart at the Ventura Mall. We'd work together for hours trying to figure out new ways to promote the products. Although different from anything I'd ever done, this kind of work really wasn't for me.

In the meantime, I turned my attention to learning as much as I could about this mysterious disease. There wasn't much, but at least I could definitely see the similarities in the symptoms other people shared. I learned about different medications, diets and exercise programs that seemed to be helping other people. I even went to a fibromyalgia support group at a local hospital. The physician leading the group talked about basically everything I'd already read about. By this time I seemed to know as much about fibromyalgia as he did! Also, many of the women in the group were complaining about their pains. Knowing what I did about Choice Theory, I knew that complaining really wasn't going to help anyone. It struck me as ironic, too, that the group didn't start until 7:00 p.m. This seemed to be an odd time to hold such a meeting (for a group of exhausted women) when I was usually in bed by 7:30!

Still, the most important thing to me wasn't my illness, but my family. I worried about Michael constantly. I just couldn't figure out what to do. Michael and I had always been close. He would have friends over all the time and I'd bring snack trays to him and his friends. Most of the time he was a good kid, but other times, he would become angry and depressed. We started him with another counselor. He never complained about going but the counseling didn't seem to be helping him. His grades were slipping in school. He decided to quit baseball so he could get a job and work.

In 1998, I read Dr. Glasser's book *Choice Theory*. I decided to try to put some of the concepts to work. Instead of focusing on my misery, I started focusing on things I could control. Although I had exercised in the past, I stopped when I became ill. So, I began walking again at night with Jeff. David would love to go along on his bike. Even Michael walked with me sometimes. It was a good chance for us to get together and talk. I also decided that as tired as I was, I might as well go to the movies with my family. I could be just as tired at the movies as I'd be at home. I was really tired of being sick and tired.

On the days I felt okay, I really began forcing myself to get out and do things. Just going out to breakfast seemed like such an event. It had been so long since I did anything like this. We went sailing with a friend several times and began going to the beach regularly. These were things that didn't take much physical effort. It wasn't much, but I was figuring out things I could do. Obviously, the housework wasn't such an issue anymore. I certainly no longer had the energy to obsess over it. Jeff now says to me that getting fibromyalgia was God's way of slowing me down. He may be right!

I knew that leaving the Institute had been a bad mistake. But what else could I have done? I simply felt too sick to do my job. I left in October of 1997. That year, Linda invited me to the employee Christmas party. I thought this was very nice, so I went. As I sat around that table at the restaurant, I realized I really missed these people. I also knew that it wasn't my job that was causing all this agony. The pain and fatigue didn't stop when I left. I wrote Linda a note sharing my thoughts. I wanted to come back to work. By now I was feeling a little better and thought I could at least put in two days a week. Linda thought it over and welcomed me back in January of 1998. It didn't take long before I was working three days a week. I could deal with this. I remember telling Jeff that as difficult as some days were, I was glad to have a job to go to and things to talk about at work that didn't have anything to do with my illness.

I started noticing the people around me, my friends, neighbors, the people I worked with. It seemed to me that the people who were healthy and happy were the people who didn't worry so much. I worried about everything: money, the house, my work and my family. I worried about my children's homework assignments more than they did. How many times over the years had I heard my kids say, "Mom, don't worry so much." I worried so much that I noticed that my muscles were always stiff and rigid.

I used to draw and spend lots of time with my pets. But somehow I'd stopped making time for the things I enjoyed. So, I began drawing with the kids. I started walking with my dog. I even snuggled with our hamster every night. Because of my allergies, we'd had to make our two cats outside pets. We put a cat door in the garage and set up kitty condos. They adapted very quickly. I found that if I walked around the neighborhood, they'd follow me. It was so cute. Kids started coming to the house again. Funny how they had stopped. I believe they must have sensed things in our home weren't as they used to be.

I began re-reading parts of *Choice Theory*. It helped me to see my relationship with Jeff in a different light. It wasn't that he was expecting me to do everything. He just didn't have housework in his quality world. I thought about all the times I had complained about how messy the house was, and how I'd made too good a use of one of the seven deadly habits that harm relationships—complaining. Dr. Glasser talks a lot about these deadly habits in some of his recent books.

But once I stopped complaining, I found that Jeff started helping out around the house on his own. If I needed something done, I'd simply ask nicely, when before I'd get angry because I figured he should know what needed to be done. He used to tell me he wasn't a mind reader. Maybe it was time I listened.

Linda was a great assistance to me in dealing with Michael. She helped me see that Michael's problems were because of the choices he was making. I needed to set limits, and not blame myself if he couldn't live within those limits. That was his choice. I didn't think our rules were too restrictive.

In 1999, just before Michael's high school graduation, he decided he wanted to move out. This was very hard on me and not at all like I'd pictured things. I tried to understand him, often talking with him until I was blue in the face. But he just seemed to want to do things his way.

I love Michael, but I began to accept that I couldn't be responsible for his behavior. All I could do was work on staying as close to him as possible, letting him know I had faith in him, and would support him in his efforts, but I couldn't fix things for him. I accepted that he had the right to live his own life and learn from his own mistakes rather than trying to meet my picture of what I wanted him to be.

Now, three years after my diagnosis, my health continues to improve. I'm not a hundred percent, but with some adjustments to the demands I've made on myself, I do just fine. If my body tells me I'm too tired to mop and wax the floor, I don't do it. I don't complain about other people not doing it either. After all, as my mother-in-law says, "The housework will always wait for you." I rarely suffer from pain and never to the degree it was. When I do start to get achy, I know it is usually because I've been overly stressing over something. When life does become stressful, I try not to get upset about what I realize I can't control. As long as I'm doing my best, I know things will work out whether I worry about it or not.

Jeff and I are spending more time together. I'm much happier now and believe he is, too. I thank God for this good man every day. I don't know what my life would be like without him. He stuck with me and I know that no matter what the future brings, we can get through it together. We were walking together on Christmas Day and he said, "Do you know what my best Christmas present was?" I said "Your motorcycle jersey?" He said, "No, my best Christmas present was seeing you happier and feeling so much better this year." That was such a nice compliment. It's my best gift, too.

I keep thinking about all the time I spent trying to change Michael and Michael's father before him. How I had such a good, loving husband, but without realizing it, I tried to change him, too. I can't say I no longer worry about things; I do because I just think it is a woman's nature. However, I am realizing more each day what I can and can't control. We've managed to keep David in private school, even with our reduced income. Money is tight. But do you know what? Jeff has never once complained. I realize he knows I do the best I can. I think he's just thankful to have me back. I do the best I can and finally, it's enough.

A Final Word

Sue's story clearly illustrates that my approach to fibromyalgia is neither medical nor psychiatric; it is strictly educational. There is nothing in this book to suggest that you or your doctor stop doing anything either of you believes is helpful. I suggest you learn to do what Sue did without the book: apply Choice Theory to the relationships in your life.

As soon as Sue read the first seven chapters, she realized how helpful it would have been to be able to resource this information when she began to suffer. When she agreed to tell her story, she told me that if she could help one person avoid what she endured, she was willing to sacrifice her privacy. I am grateful for her contribution.

The Choice Theory ideas are effective because accepting that you are the only person you can control, and controlling yourself less than many of you are trying to do now, is essential to the process. As far as we know, we are the only people who teach Choice Theory, so please feel free to share this book with your doctor or with anyone else who may be interested. If you have received help from reading this material, we would appreciate your writing and telling us about your experience.

To learn more about Choice Theory or how to arrange for one of our instructors to make a presentation to an interested group (lay or professional), we invite you to call the William Glasser Institute (See Appendix B) and ask for Linda or Sue.

ENDNOTES

1. Published in the Nov. 13, 2000 issue of the *New Yorker*, "Hurting All Over," by Jerome Groopman, M.D., pp 78-92.

2. *Choice Theory: A New Psychology of Personal Freedom*, by William Glasser, HarperCollins, New York, 1998.

3. For further information on the effects of psychotropic drugs, consult these books by Peter Breggin: *Your Drug May Be Your Problem*, Perseus Books, Reading, Massachusetts, 2000 and *Toxic Psychiatry*, St. Martins Press, New York, 1991.

4. Although it is acknowledged that Margaret Mitchell is the author of the book, we are more familiar with Clark Gable's rendition of this now immortal line in the 1939 movie (from the book by the same name), *Gone With the Wind*.

APPENDIX A
Suggested Reading Material

Unless otherwise noted, the following books by William Glasser, M.D., are published by HarperCollins and are available or can be ordered at most bookstores. All of Dr. Glasser's books also can be ordered directly from William Glasser, Inc., which is housed at the William Glasser Institute (see Appendix B). For pricing, which includes postage and handling, refer to the Institute website, www.wglasser.com.

Choice Theory, 1998, paperback.

> This is the basic book on Choice Theory Psychology. It explains the theory and how it differs markedly from the destructive world psychology that Dr. Glasser calls *external control psychology*. The way it is explained, the reader can begin to use it in every aspect of his or her life.

Reality Therapy In Action, 2000, hardcover. (A paperback edition of this book will be released in May 2001 and retitled *Counseling With Choice Theory, The New Reality Therapy*.)

> In this updated and expanded edition of the 1965 *Reality Therapy*, Dr. Glasser takes readers into his consulting room and illustrates, through a series of conversations with his patients, exactly how he puts his theories into practice. It is similar in style to Dr. Glasser's session with Ellen in Chapter Seven of this book on fibromyalgia.

The Language of Choice Theory, 2000, paperback.

This book explains how to use Choice Theory to replace external control language in four major areas: parents as they talk to their children, husbands and wives as they talk to each other, teachers as they talk to students, and managers as they talk to workers. The difference between Choice Theory and external control is brought to life here. Readers will recognize themselves and all the people they know in its many examples.

Getting Together and Staying Together, 2000, paperback.

Here Choice Theory is applied to finding a mate and living happily after marriage. Dr. and Mrs. Glasser explain how they use these ideas in their own marriage. This book also provides insights into the reasons for unhappy marriages and creative solutions for putting the happiness back in.

What Is This Thing Called Love? The Essential Book for the Single Woman, 2000, paperback.

Single women learn how to apply Choice Theory to their relationships, especially how to deal with a man who is reluctant to commit to marriage. For those who have had a bad experience with a man who professes love, this book provides new information and understanding.

Every Student Can Succeed, 2000, paperback (only available through William Glasser, Inc.)

This useful book for parents, teachers and teacher educators demonstrates what to do and say to reach the challenging students a teacher faces. In this book Dr. Glasser shows how schools and classes can be places of joy where students want to engage in quality work.

*****

The following books by Dr. Peter Breggin and Dr. David Cohen, available in all bookstores, explain that there is no pathology in the brains of people who are now diagnosed with what are called mental illnesses unless the pathology is obvious, such as in Alzheimer's Disease. These books, which Dr. Glasser refers to in Chapter Four of this book (see the Endnotes), show how psychiatric drugs harm the brain.

Toxic Psychiatry, Peter Breggin, M.D., 1991, hardcover and paperback, St. Martins Press, New York.

Through his painstaking review of psychiatric research, Dr. Breggin explains that there is no pathology in the brain and that mental illness, even what is now labeled schizophrenia and clinical depression, can be as successfully treated with caring psychotherapy as it can with potentially harmful psychiatric drugs.

Your Drug May Be Your Problem, How and Why to Stop Taking Psychiatric Medications, Peter Breggin, M.D. and David Cohen Ph.D., 1999, hardcover and paperback, Perseus Books, HarperCollins, New York.

This book documents the dangers of taking psychiatric drugs for all conditions. It is well worth reading for those who are on any psychiatric medication and are not getting the expected benefit from it.

APPENDIX B
The William Glasser Institute

In 1967, I founded the Institute for Reality Therapy for the purpose of teaching that approach to counselors, educators, managers, and literally anyone who worked with people. Since its inception, I have greatly expanded my thinking with the addition of Choice Theory and have applied that theory to almost every aspect of Reality Therapy. I have also extended the use of Choice Theory into the schools, as exemplified by the quality school program, and into managing for quality in all other areas in which people are managed. My ideas are being applied to an entire community in Corning, New York.

With all these expansions and applications, I have gone so far beyond Reality Therapy that, for accuracy, I was encouraged to change the name of the Institute to the William Glasser Institute. In 1996 I made the change so that anyone who is interested in any of my ideas and their application could easily contact us. Over the years, as our teaching and training have expanded, satellite organizations have been set up in many countries around the world.

The Institute, under the leadership of Linda Harshman, coordinates and monitors all training and serves as an information clearinghouse. My latest thinking is often made available through audiotapes, videotapes and publications. The *International Journal of Reality Therapy,* produced at Northeastern University, is the research arm of the Institute and serves as a vehicle through which its members can publish their works on new ways of using and teaching Reality Therapy.

As mentioned, the basic effort of the William Glasser Institute centers on providing training for professionals who want to use my ideas in their work with others. There are five parts to this training, which takes a minimum of eighteen months to complete: Basic Intensive Week, Basic Practicum, Advanced Intensive Week, Advanced Practicum and the Certification Week. All of the instruction is done in small groups, and by explanation, discussion and demonstration. Upon successful completion of the process, the individual is awarded a certificate that states he or she is Reality Therapy Certified. The certificate is not a license to practice counseling or psychotherapy. These practices are governed by the appropriate licensing authorities in various legal jurisdictions in North America and in other countries.

The Institute employs user-friendly people trained in Choice Theory, so if you contact us, you can be sure of a courteous response. It is my vision to teach Choice Theory to the world. I invite you to join me in this effort.

For further information about my work, including my lectures, books, and audio and video materials as well as the Institute programs, contact:

The William Glasser Institute
22024 Lassen Street, Suite 118
Chatsworth, CA 91311
Phone: 800-899-0688; 818-700-8000
Fax: 818-700-0555
E-mail: wginst@earthlink.net
Web: www.wglasser.com

Author's Biography

William Glasser, M.D. is the president of the William Glasser Institute, an organization of over six thousand Reality Therapy Certified people who teach and practice Choice Theory and Reality Therapy all over the world. He is a board-certified psychiatrist who has written over fifteen books, which HarperCollins has published. These books have been translated into almost every major language and have sold more than two million copies. The best known of these are *Reality Therapy*, *Schools Without Failure* and *Choice Theory: A New Psychology of Personal Freedom*.

He has worked in every aspect of psychiatry, and for nine years was the psychiatrist for the Los Angeles Orthopedic Hospital where he specialized in dealing with chronic pain and disability of unknown origin. He has also worked for over forty years in public schools and is known for this work all over the world. He is a board member of The International Center for the Study of Psychiatry founded and directed by Dr. Peter Breggin. This center is dedicated to bringing compassion and caring back into mental health and fighting against the overuse and inappropriate use of psychiatric drugs. Dr. Glasser teaches and lectures all over the world. For more information log on to **www.wglasser.com.**